Ikenaga 2 Jos Leys

"A relatively simple formula can generate immensely complex images." – **Jos Leys**

Investigations

IN NUMBER, DATA, AND SPACE®

PEARSON

Glenview, Illinois • Boston, Massachusetts
Chandler, Arizona • Upper Saddle River, New Jersey

T E R C

The Investigations curriculum was developed by TERC, Cambridge, MA.

This material is based on work supported by the National Science Foundation ("NSF") under Grant No. ESI-0095450. Any opinions, findings, and conclusions or recommendations expressed in this material are those of the author(s) and do not necessarily reflect the views of the National Science Foundation.

ISBN-13: 978-0-328-60020-5

ISBN-10: 0-328-60020-2

5 6 7 8 9 10 V064 16 15 14

T E R C

Co-Principal Investigators

Susan Jo Russell

Karen Economopoulos

Authors

Lucy Wittenberg
Director Grades 3–5

Karen Economopoulos
Director Grades K–2

Virginia Bastable
(SummerMath for Teachers,
Mt. Holyoke College)

Katie Hickey Bloomfield

Keith Cochran

Darrell Earnest

Arusha Hollister

Nancy Horowitz

Erin Leidl

Megan Murray

Young Oh

Beth W. Perry

Susan Jo Russell

Deborah Schifter
(Education
Development Center)

Kathy Sillman

Administrative Staff

Amy Taber
Project Manager

Beth Bergeron

Lorraine Brooks

Emi Fujiwara

Contributing Authors

Denise Baumann

Jennifer DiBrienza

Hollee Freeman

Paula Hooper

Jan Mokros

Stephen Monk
(University of Washington)

Mary Beth O'Connor

Judy Storeygard

Cornelia Tierney

Elizabeth Van Cleef

Carol Wright

Technology

Jim Hammerman

Classroom Field Work

Amy Appell

Rachel E. Davis

Traci Higgins

Julia Thompson

Collaborating Teachers

This group of dedicated teachers carried out extensive field testing in their classrooms, met regularly to discuss issues of teaching and learning mathematics, provided feedback to staff, welcomed staff into their classrooms to document students' work, and contributed both suggestions and written material that has been incorporated into the curriculum.

Bethany Altchek

Linda Amaral

Kimberly Beauregard

Barbara Bernard

Nancy Buell

Rose Christiansen

Chris Colbath-Hess

Lisette Colon

Kim Cook

Frances Cooper

Kathleen Drew

Rebeka Eston Salemi

Thomas Fisher

Michael Flynn

Holly Ghazey

Susan Gillis

Danielle Harrington

Elaine Herzog

Francine Hiller

Kirsten Lee Howard

Liliana Klass

Leslie Kramer

Melissa Lee Andrichak

Kelley Lee Sadowski

Jennifer Levitan

Mary Lou LoVecchio

Kristen McEnaney

Maura McGrail

Kathe Millett

Florence Molyneaux

Amy Monkiewicz

Elizabeth Monopoli

Carol Murray

Robyn Musser

Christine Norrman

Deborah O'Brien

Timothy O'Connor

Anne Marie O'Reilly

Mark Paige

Margaret Riddle

Karen Schweitzer

Elisabeth Seyferth

Susan Smith

Debra Sorvillo

Shoshanah Starr

Janice Szymaszek

Karen Tobin

JoAnn Trauschke

Ana Vaisenstein

Yvonne Watson

Michelle Woods

Mary Wright

Advisors

Deborah Lowenberg Ball,
University of Michigan

Hyman Bass, Professor of Mathematics and Mathematics Education
University of Michigan

Mary Canner, Principal, Natick Public Schools

Thomas Carpenter, Professor of Curriculum and Instruction,
University of Wisconsin-Madison

Janis Freckmann, Elementary Mathematics Coordinator,
Milwaukee Public Schools

Lynne Godfrey, Mathematics Coach,
Cambridge Public Schools

Ginger Hanlon, Instructional Specialist in Mathematics,
New York City Public Schools

DeAnn Huinker, Director, Center for Mathematics and
Science Education Research, University of Wisconsin-Milwaukee

James Kaput, Professor of Mathematics, University of
Massachusetts-Dartmouth

Kate Kline, Associate Professor, Department of Mathematics
and Statistics, Western Michigan University

Jim Lewis, Professor of Mathematics,
University of Nebraska-Lincoln

William McCallum, Professor of Mathematics,
University of Arizona

Harriet Pollatsek, Professor of Mathematics,
Mount Holyoke College

Debra Shein-Gerson, Elementary Mathematics Specialist,
Weston Public Schools

Gary Shevell, Assistant Principal,
New York City Public Schools

Liz Sweeney, Elementary Math Department,
Boston Public Schools

Lucy West, Consultant, Metamorphosis:
Teaching Learning Communities, Inc.

This revision of the curriculum was built on the work of the many authors who contributed to the first edition (published between 1994 and 1998). We acknowledge the critical contributions of these authors in developing the content and pedagogy of *Investigations*:

Authors

Joan Akers

Michael T. Battista

Douglas H. Clements

Karen Economopoulos

Marlene Kliman

Jan Mokros

Megan Murray

Ricardo Nemirovsky

Andee Rubin

Susan Jo Russell

Cornelia Tierney

Contributing Authors

Mary Berle-Carman

Rebecca B. Corwin

Rebeka Eston

Claryce Evans

Anne Goodrow

Cliff Konold

Chris Mainhart

Sue McMillen

Jerrie Moffet

Tracy Noble

Kim O'Neil

Mark Ogonowski

Julie Sarama

Amy Shulman Weinberg

Margie Singer

Virginia Woolley

Tracey Wright

Contents

UNIT 1

Trading Stickers, Combining Coins

Investigations

Overview of Program Components

FOR TEACHERS

The **Curriculum Units** are the teaching guides. (See far right.)

Implementing Investigations in Grade 3 offers suggestions for implementing the curriculum. It also contains a comprehensive index.

The **Differentiation and Intervention Guide** offers additional activities for each Investigation to support the range of learners.

Investigations for the Interactive Whiteboard provides whole-class instructional support to enhance each session.

The **Resource Masters and Transparencies CD** contains all reproducible materials that support instruction. The **LogoPaths CD** provides an environment in which students investigate a variety of geometric ideas.

FOR STUDENTS

The **Student Activity Book** contains the consumable student pages (Recording Sheets, Homework, Practice, and so on).

The **Student Math Handbook** contains Math Words and Ideas pages and Games directions.

The *Investigations* Curriculum

Investigations in Number, Data, and Space® is a K–5 mathematics curriculum designed to engage students in making sense of mathematical ideas. Six major goals guided the development of the *Investigations in Number, Data, and Space*® curriculum. The curriculum is designed to:

- Support students to make sense of mathematics and learn that they can be mathematical thinkers

- Focus on computational fluency with whole numbers as a major goal of the elementary grades

- Provide substantive work in important areas of mathematics—rational numbers, geometry, measurement, data, and early algebra—and connections among them

- Emphasize reasoning about mathematical ideas

- Communicate mathematics content and pedagogy to teachers

- Engage the range of learners in understanding mathematics

Underlying these goals are three guiding principles that are touchstones for the *Investigations* team as we approach both students and teachers as agents of their own learning:

1. *Students have mathematical ideas.* Students come to school with ideas about numbers, shapes, measurements, patterns, and data. If given the opportunity to learn in an environment that stresses making sense of mathematics, students build on the ideas they already have and learn about new mathematics they have never encountered. Students learn that they are capable of having mathematical ideas, applying what they know to new situations, and thinking and reasoning about unfamiliar problems.

2. *Teachers are engaged in ongoing learning* about mathematics content, pedagogy, and student learning. The curriculum provides material for professional development, to be used by teachers individually or in groups, that supports teachers' continued learning as they use the curriculum over several years. The *Investigations* curriculum materials are designed as much to be a dialogue with teachers as to be a core of content for students.

3. *Teachers collaborate with the students and curriculum materials* to create the curriculum as enacted in the classroom. The only way for a good curriculum to be used well is for teachers to be active participants in implementing it. Teachers use the curriculum to maintain a clear, focused, and coherent agenda for mathematics teaching. At the same time, they observe and listen carefully to students, try to understand how they are thinking, and make teaching decisions based on these observations.

Investigations is based on experience from research and practice, including field testing that involved documentation of thousands of hours in classrooms, observations of students, input from teachers, and analysis of student work. As a result, the curriculum addresses the learning needs of real students in a wide range of classrooms and communities. The investigations are carefully designed to invite all students into mathematics—girls and boys; members of diverse cultural, ethnic, and language groups; and students with a wide variety of strengths, needs, and interests.

Based on this extensive classroom testing, the curriculum takes seriously the time students need to develop a strong conceptual foundation and skills based on that foundation. Each curriculum unit focuses on an area of content in depth, providing time for students to develop and practice ideas across a variety of activities and contexts that build on each other. Daily guidelines for time spent on class sessions, Classroom Routines (K–3), and Ten-Minute Math (3–5) reflect the commitment to devoting adequate time to mathematics in each school day.

About This Curriculum Unit

This **Curriculum Unit** is one of nine teaching guides in Grade 3. The first unit in Grade 3 is *Trading Stickers, Combining Coins*.

- The **Introduction and Overview** section organizes and presents the instructional materials, provides background information, and highlights important features specific to this unit.

- Each Curriculum Unit contains several **Investigations.** Each Investigation focuses on a set of related mathematical ideas.

- Investigations are divided into one-hour **Sessions,** or lessons.

- Sessions have a combination of these parts: **Activity, Discussion, Math Workshop, Assessment Activity,** and **Session Follow-Up.**

- Each session also has one or more **Classroom Routines and Ten-Minute Math** activities that are done outside of math time.

- At the back of the book is a collection of **Teacher Notes** and **Dialogue Boxes** that provide professional development related to the unit.

- Also included at the back of the book are the **Student Math Handbook** pages for this unit.,

- The **Index** provides a way to look up important words or terms.

Overview

OF THIS UNIT

Investigation	Session	Day	
INVESTIGATION 1 **Hundreds, Tens, and Ones** Students represent the place value of numbers by using a base-ten model, money, 100 grids, and number lines. They add and subtract multiples of 10 and use knowledge of place value to find combinations with a sum of 100 and 200.	**1.1** Stickers: A Base-Ten Model	1	
	1.2 Adding and Subtracting 2-Digit Numbers	2	
	1.3 More Than Ten Ones	3	
	1.4 How Many More Stickers to Get 100?	4	
	1.5 Capture 5: Adding and Subtracting 10s and 1s	5	
	1.6 Assessment: Adding and Subtracting 10s	6	
	1.7 Strategies for Capture 5	7	
	1.8 Making Numbers with 100s, 10s, and 1s	8	
	1.9 Assessment: Hundreds, Tens, and Ones	9	
INVESTIGATION 2 **Working with 100** Students solve addition, subtraction, and missing addend problems that involve combinations with a sum of 100, using money and other contexts. They find equivalent ways to show quantities with hundreds, tens, and ones and review addition combinations up to 10 + 10.	**2.1** Addition Combinations	10	
	2.2 Close to 100	11	
	2.3 More or Less Than 100?	12	
	2.4 Coin Combinations	13	
	2.5 Assessment: Addition Combinations	14	
	2.6 Story Problem Strategies	15	
	2.7 163 Stickers	16	
	2.8 End-of-Unit Assessment	17	

Each *Investigations* session has some combination of these five parts: **Activity, Discussion, Math Workshop, Assessment Activity,** and **Session Follow-Up.** These session parts are indicated in the chart below. Each session also has one **Classroom Routine or Ten-Minute Math** activity that is done outside of math time.

 Ⓦ Interactive Whiteboard

Activity	Discussion	Math Workshop	Assessment Activity	Session Follow-Up
Ⓦ ● Ⓦ				●
Ⓦ	Ⓦ			●
●	Ⓦ Ⓦ			●
Ⓦ ●	Ⓦ			●
Ⓦ ●				●
Ⓦ		●	●	●
	Ⓦ	●		●
Ⓦ Ⓦ	Ⓦ			●
	Ⓦ		●	●
Ⓦ ●				●
Ⓦ ●				●
Ⓦ	Ⓦ	●		●
Ⓦ Ⓦ ●				●
		●	●	●
	Ⓦ	●		●
	Ⓦ	●		●
			Ⓦ	●

Ten-Minute Math

Practicing Place Value	*More or Less?*
Ⓦ	
Ⓦ	
Ⓦ	
Ⓦ	
Ⓦ	
Ⓦ	
Ⓦ	
Ⓦ	
Ⓦ	
Ⓦ	
Ⓦ	
	Ⓦ
	Ⓦ
	Ⓦ
	Ⓦ
	Ⓦ
	Ⓦ

Mathematics

Trading Stickers, Combining Coins is the first Grade 3 unit in the number and operations strand of *Investigations*. These units develop ideas about the meaning of operations with whole numbers, the development of computational fluency, the structure of place value and the base-ten number system, and generalizations about numbers and operations.

LOOKING BACK This unit assumes that students in Grade 3 bring with them the ability to use a place value model to represent a number as 10s and 1s, an understanding of the magnitude and sequence of numbers to 100, and knowledge of addition combinations to 10 + 10. In Grade 2, students explored the properties of addition and subtraction and developed an understanding of the relationship between these two operations. Students learned to write addition or subtraction equations to represent these operations. They also began to develop fluency with strategies for addition of 2-digit numbers. They worked on subtraction problems of several types, including removal and finding a missing part. Students should have strategies for solving subtraction problems accurately, but these may not yet be fluent and efficient. Students used manipulatives, drawings, tools, and notation to show strategies and solutions. There was a particular emphasis on the 100 chart and number line to model problems and to record strategies for adding and subtracting two 2-digit numbers.

This unit focuses on 2 Mathematical Emphases:

1 The Base-Ten Number System Understanding the equivalence of one group and the units that comprise it

Math Focus Points

◆ Recognizing and representing the place value of each digit in 2- and 3-digit numbers

◆ Using equivalencies among pennies, dimes, and dollars

◆ Finding different combinations of 100s, 10s, and 1s for a number and recognizing their equivalence (i.e. 1 hundred, 3 tens, and 7 ones equals 1 hundred, 2 tens, and 17 ones, or 13 tens and 7 ones)

◆ Recognizing and demonstrating the equivalence of one 100 to ten 10s and of one 10 to ten 1s

◆ Recognizing and using coin equivalencies

An important part of students' mathematical work in the elementary grades is building an understanding of the base-ten number system. In this unit, students build on and extend the base-ten context of stickers (introduced in Grade 2) to represent the place value of 2- and 3-digit numbers.

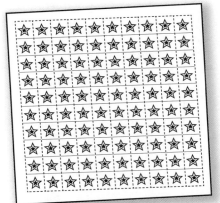

Sheet of 100 stickers

Stickers come in strips of 10 and singles.

Students compose numbers by using stickers that come in sheets of 100, strips of 10, and singles. They identify the hundreds digit as representing how many 100s are in the number, the tens digit as representing how many 10s, and the ones digit as representing how many 1s. In other words, they learn to identify a number such as 137 as representing 1 hundred, 3 tens, and 7 ones. Flexibility in breaking numbers into 100s, 10s, and 1s in different ways is an important component of developing computational fluency. Thus, it is crucial that students understand that 137 is also composed of 1 hundred, 2 tens, and 17 ones; 13 tens and 7 ones; 12 tens and 17 ones; 11 tens and 27 ones; and so forth. Students develop this understanding as they use different combinations of stickers to represent 137.

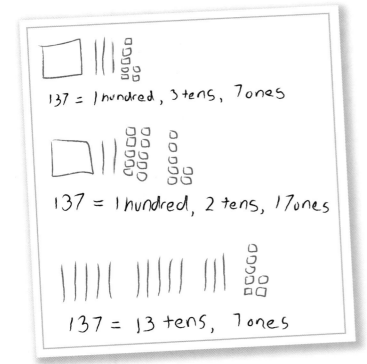

Students also develop an understanding of the relationship between 100s, 10s, and 1s through activities and problems in which they accumulate and trade dollars, dimes, and pennies.

2 Computational Fluency Adding and subtracting accurately and efficiently

Math Focus Points

- Adding and subtracting multiples of 10

- Solving addition problems with 2-digit numbers by using strategies that involve breaking numbers apart by place or adding one number in parts

- Solving addition problems with 2-digit numbers that involve more than 10 ones in the ones place and explaining the effect on the sum

- Finding the difference between a 2-digit number and 100

- Adding pennies and dimes to sums up to $2.00

- Learning/reviewing addition combinations up to 10 + 10

- Using knowledge of place value to find pairs of 2-digit numbers that add to 100 or a number close to 100

- Using known pairs of 2-digit numbers that add to 100 to find related pairs that add to 100 or a number close to 100 (for example, 20 + 80 = 100, so 22 + 78 = 100)

- Estimating the sums of 2-digit numbers by using knowledge of place value and known combinations

- Finding combinations of coins that equal $1.00

To develop efficient computation strategies, students must be fluent with addition combinations to 10 + 10. It is expected that students learned these combinations in Grade 2; however, some third-grade students may need additional work on some combinations, and all students will benefit from the review and practice of these combinations in this unit.

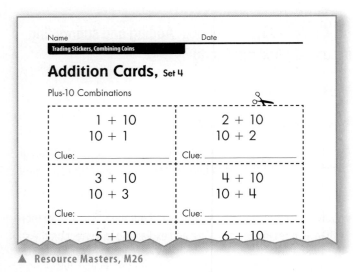

▲ Resource Masters, M26

The development of accurate and efficient computation strategies also involves the ability to add multiples of 10 to, and subtract them from, any number. In Investigation 1, students first use a place value context to examine what happens when 10 or a multiple of 10 is added to or subtracted from a 2- or 3-digit number. They look at what happens to the digit in the ones place and explain why this digit does not change.

$$47 + 10 = 57$$

$$47 + 30 = 77$$

$$47 - 10 = 37$$

$$47 - 20 = 27$$

Students apply their understanding of place value and the ability to add 10s as they solve a variety of addition problems in this unit. They use strategies involving adding by place or adding one number in parts. See **Teacher Note:** Addition Strategies, page 149. Although developing specific subtraction strategies is not a focus of this unit, students solve subtraction problems involving 2-digit numbers in both Investigations 1 and 2 to prepare for focused work on subtraction in later units.

Computational fluency also involves the use of known combinations to solve more difficult problems. In Investigation 1, students solve problems in which they find the difference between a given quantity and 100, or between a given amount of money and a dollar. In Investigation 2, students use their knowledge of place value and known combinations with a sum of 100 to find other pairs of 2-digit numbers with sums of 100 and combinations of coins that add to a dollar. These activities develop an understanding of the importance of 100 as a landmark in our number system. They also prepare students to use the relationship of 100 to other numbers to solve computation problems.

▲ Resource Masters, M40

This Unit also focuses on

◆ Using mathematical tools (cubes, 100 charts and grids, number lines) to solve problems and represent strategies.

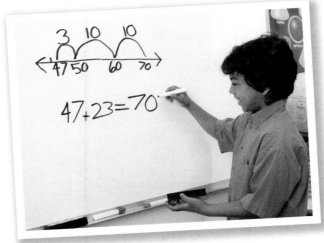

An unmarked number line is one of the tools students learn to use for solving problems.

Classroom Routines focus on

◆ Learning about temperature: reading a thermometer, learning to associate different temperatures with words such as *colder* and *warmer*, establishing landmark temperatures

◆ Recording information in a table and on a graph

◆ Reading information from the shape of a graph: hot, cold, increasing, decreasing

Ten-Minute Math activities focus on

◆ Recognizing and interpreting the value of each digit in 2- and 3-digit numbers

◆ Finding different combinations of a number, using only 100s, 10s, and 1s and recognizing their equivalence (e.g., 1 hundred, 3 tens, and 7 ones equals 1 hundred, 2 tens, and 17 ones or 13 tens and 7 ones)

◆ Reading and writing 2- and 3-digit numbers

◆ Adding multiples of 10 to, and subtracting multiples of 10 from, 2- and 3-digit numbers

◆ Breaking apart, reordering, or combining numbers within a problem for easier computation

◆ Using knowledge of place value and known combinations to estimate sums

◆ Practicing addition and subtraction skills

LOOKING FORWARD Later in Grade 3, students extend their understanding of place value as they construct 1,000 from units of 100. They continue to develop and examine strategies for addition and are expected to leave Grade 3 having at least one strategy they can use accurately and efficiently to solve addition problems involving 2- and 3-digit numbers. Students solve subtraction problems in a variety of contexts, moving from counting on and counting back, to solving these problems by adding and subtracting in chunks. They are expected to leave Grade 3 able to solve 2- and small 3-digit subtraction problems.

In Grade 4, students extend their understanding of the number system to 10,000. They examine strategies for addition, including the U.S. algorithm. They are also expected to leave Grade 4 fluent in this operation, having at least one strategy they use efficiently, while having access to an understanding of other possible strategies. They continue to refine their subtraction strategies and are expected to leave the grade with at least one subtraction strategy they use fluently and efficiently. In Grade 5, students encounter one more unit on addition and subtraction, in which they apply their knowledge of both operations to problems with large numbers. They study the operation of subtraction in much the same way that they did for addition in Grade 4, including the U.S. algorithm for subtraction. It is intended that their work with these two operations and whole numbers will be complete by the end of Grade 5.

Assessment

IN THIS UNIT

ONGOING ASSESSMENT: Observing Students at Work

The following sessions provide **Ongoing Assessment: Observing Students at Work** opportunities:

- **Session 1.1, p. 32**
- **Session 1.2, p. 42**
- **Session 1.3, p. 49**
- **Session 1.4, p. 55**
- **Session 1.5, p. 63**
- **Session 1.6, pp. 69 and 70**

- **Session 1.7, p. 75**
- **Session 1.8, p. 80**
- **Session 1.9, p. 89**
- **Session 2.1, p. 100**
- **Session 2.2, p. 107**
- **Session 2.3, pp. 112 and 113**

- **Session 2.4, pp. 118 and 119**
- **Session 2.5, pp. 123 and 124**
- **Session 2.6, p. 131**
- **Session 2.7, p. 136**
- **Session 2.8, p. 140**

WRITING OPPORTUNITIES

The following sessions have **writing** opportunities for students to explain their mathematical thinking:

- **Session 1.2, p. 43**
  Student Activity Book, p. 11

- **Session 1.6, p. 70**
  Student Activity Book, p. 24

- **Session 2.2, p. 108**
  Student Activity Book, p. 40

- **Session 2.3, p. 112**
  Student Activity Book, pp. 41–42

- **Session 2.7, pp. 136 and 138**
  Student Activity Book, pp. 55–56

PORTFOLIO OPPORTUNITIES

The following sessions have work appropriate for a **portfolio:**

- **Session 1.2, p. 40**
  Student Activity Book, pp. 9–10

- **Session 1.4, p. 55**
  Student Activity Book, pp. 15–16

- **Session 1.9, p. 88**
  M21–M22, Assessment: Hundreds, Tens, and Ones

- **Session 2.3, p. 112**
  Student Activity Book, pp. 41–42

- **Session 2.5, p. 122**
  M44, Assessment: Addition Combinations

- **Session 2.7, p. 136**
  Student Activity Book, p. 55

- **Session 2.8, p. 140**
  M46–M48, End-of-Unit Assessment

Assessing the Benchmarks

Observing students as they engage in conversation about their ideas is a primary means to assess their mathematical understanding. Consider all of your students' work, not just the written assessments. See the chart below for suggestions about key activities to observe.

See the **Differentiation and Intervention Guide** for quizzes that can be used after each Investigation.

Benchmarks in This Unit	Key Activities to Observe	Assessment
1. Demonstate fluency with the addition combinations up to 10 + 10.	**Session 2.1:** Combinations I Know and Combinations I'm Working On	**Session 2.5 Assessment Activity:** Addition Combinations
2. Add multiples of 10 (up to 100) to and subtract them from 2- and small 3-digit numbers.	**Session 1.1:** Adding and Subtracting 10s Problems **Sessions 1.5–1.7:** *Capture 5*	**Sessions 1.6–1.7 Assessment:** Adding and Subtracting 10s 
3. Solve addition problems with 2-digit numbers using strategies that involve breaking numbers apart by place or adding one number in parts.	**Session 1.2:** Adding and Subtracting 10s and 1s	**Session 1.9 Assessment: Hundreds, Tens, and Ones** Problem 1, Part A **Session 2.8 End-of-Unit Assessment:** Problem 1
4. Break up 3-digit numbers (less than 200) into 100s, 10s, and 1s in different ways (e.g., 153 equals 1 hundred, 5 tens, and 3 ones; 15 tens and 3 ones; 14 tens and 13 ones, etc.).	**Session 1.8:** Sticker Combinations: 137 Stickers **Session 2.6:** Sheets, Strips, and Singles	**Session 1.9 Assessment: Hundreds, Tens, and Ones** Problem 2 **Session 2.8 End-of-Unit Assessment:** Problem 3
5. Find combinations of 2-digit numbers that add to 100 or $1.00.	**Sessions 2.2–2.3 and 2.5–2.7:** *Close to 100* **Sessions 2.4–2.7:** *Make a Dollar*	**Session 1.9 Assessment: Hundreds, Tens, and Ones** Problem 1, Part B **Session 2.8 End-of-Unit Assessment:** Problem 2

✓ Checklist Available

Relating the Mathematical Emphases to the Benchmarks

Mathematical Emphases	Benchmarks
The Base-Ten Number System Understanding the equivalence of one group and the units that comprise it	4
Computational Fluency Adding and subtracting accurately and efficiently	1, 2, 3, and 5

Algebra Connections

IN THIS UNIT

This unit presents students with opportunities to engage with ideas that lay a foundation for algebra. Eight- and nine-year-olds can and do think algebraically. Part of the work in Grade 3 is helping students learn to verbalize those thoughts and begin considering such questions as these: "Is this statement *always* true?" "Does it work for *all* numbers?" "How can we know?" Such discussions allow students to engage in generalizations about number and operations. They also provide a foundation for meaningful use of algebraic notation in the future.

Consider the following ways that students computed $73 + 26$:

Keith: $73 + 10 = 83$

$83 + 10 = 93$

$93 + 6 = 99$

Adam: $70 + 20 = 90$

$3 + 6 = 9$

$90 + 9 = 99$

Gina: $73 + 26$ is the same as $70 + 29$. I just moved the 3. The answer is 99.

It is important to notice in all these approaches the strategic use of 10s. All of these students recognize when working with 2-digit numbers that it is easier to add multiples of 10, but each student uses this insight in a different way. Implicit in each student's work is a generalization.

Keith's Way

Keith demonstrates his strategy on the class number line. "Start at 73. Then jump 10 to 83 and 10 more to 93. That's adding 20. Then jump 6 and you land at 99."

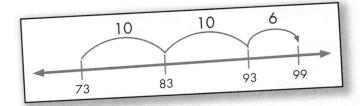

Keith decomposes 26 into $20 + 6$. First he adds the 20 (10 at a time), and then the 6, onto 73. This regrouping of addends is an example of the Associative Property: $73 + (20 + 6) = (73 + 20) + 6$.

Adam's Way

Adam uses stickers to explain his strategy. He lays out the stickers as seen below and describes what he is doing. "It's like 7 strips and 3 singles, and 2 strips and 6 singles."

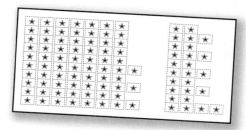

He then puts the two groups of stickers together as seen below. "Put the strips together, and put the singles together, and then add them all up. It's 99."

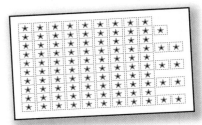

Adam decomposes 73 and 26 into 10s and 1s, producing four addends: $73 + 26 = (70 + 3) + (20 + 6)$. Then he groups the 10s together and the 1s together: $(70 + 20) + (3 + 6)$. He employs the idea that, no matter how many addends you have, you can change the grouping and the order and the total still stays the same.

In an effort to make this idea more explicit, the teacher asks, "Did you notice how Adam switched the numbers around and regrouped them? Can you always add like that—put the strips together, put the singles together, and then add?" Adam nods and explains, "Yes, you can always do it. I didn't put any more on and I didn't take any away, so it's always the same amount."

Gina's Way

Gina explains that she "took 3 from 73 and gave it to 26. It's easy to add $70 + 29$." When asked to demonstrate, Gina uses Adam's strips and singles to show how she transformed the original problem. "If you take 3 singles from the 73 and give them to the 26, you have $70 + 29$."

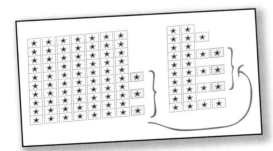

Teacher: What do you all think about what Gina did?

Edwin: It's the same as what Adam said. Gina didn't put any more on or take any away, so it's the same amount. She took some from 73 and gave it to 26, and it will always work.

Zhang: I did something like what Keith did, but I thought about stickers like Adam. First take the 7 strips from 73 and give them to the 26. That makes 96. Then add the 3 singles.

At this point, the students anticipate that the teacher will ask whether this always works. Before she can ask, Elena speaks up. "You can always take the strips and add them first and then add on the singles."

The goal is for students to use their own language to express algebraic ideas that, when they are older, they will learn to express with algebraic notation. For instance, the idea behind each child's strategy can be written algebraically.

Keith's way: $k + (m + n) = (k + m) + n$

Adam's way: $(a + b) + (c + d) = (a + c) + (b + d)$

Gina's way: $x + y = (x - z) + (y + z)$

For most adults, such notation (the use of variables, operations, and equal signs) is the chief identifying feature of algebra. The notation, however, expresses rules about how operations work, which students can reason out for themselves. This reasoning about how numbers can be put together and taken apart under different operations, and not the notation, is the work of elementary students in algebra.

In fact, the examples shown above illustrate the kind of early algebraic reasoning that is fully accessible to elementary-aged students. In *Investigations,* students are encouraged to verbalize the generalizations they see about numbers and operations and to explain and justify them by using materials and tools such as cubes, sticker strips, number lines, and 100 charts. These discussions are not so much about finding an answer to a particular problem, but about describing a strategy for finding answers to a whole class of problems.

Note: In the text for the sessions, you will find Algebra Notes that identify where these early algebra discussions are likely to arise. Some of the **Teacher Notes** and **Dialogue Boxes** further elaborate the ideas and illustrate students' conversations about them.

IN THIS UNIT

The **Classroom Routines** and **Ten-Minute Math** activities, to be done in ten minutes outside of math class, are introduced in a unit and repeated throughout the grade. Specific directions for the day's activity are provided in each session. For the full description and variations of the Classroom Routines and Ten-Minute Math activities, see *Implementing Investigations in Grade 3*.

Activity	Introduced	Full Description of Activity and Its Variations
Classroom Routines: *What's the Temperature?*	Unit 1, Session 1.1 (this unit)	*Implementing Investigations in Grade 3*
Ten-Minute Math: *Practicing Place Value*	Unit 1, Session 1.1 (this unit)	*Implementing Investigations in Grade 3*
Ten-Minute Math: *More or Less?*	Unit 1, Session 2.3 (this unit)	*Implementing Investigations in Grade 3*

What's the Temperature?

Students record the outside temperature every Wednesday morning on a chart and on a graph. This data will be used in the unit *Stories, Tables, and Graphs,* when students describe changes in temperature over time.

Math Focus Points

◆ Learning about temperature: reading a thermometer, learning to associate different temperatures with words like *colder* and *warmer,* and establishing landmark temperatures

◆ Recording information in a table and on a graph

◆ Reading information from the shape of a graph: hot, cold, increasing, decreasing

Practicing Place Value

Students practice reading, writing, and saying numbers and identifying the place value of digits in the number. They add and subtract multiples of 10 to these numbers and examine how these operations increase or decrease the values of the digits in each place. In the variations, students use cubes to represent numbers and make comparisons, and break 3-digit numbers into 100s, 10s, and 1s in different ways.

Math Focus Points

◆ Recognizing and interpreting the value of each digit in 2- and 3-digit numbers

◆ Finding different combinations of a number, using only 100s, 10s, and 1s and recognizing their equivalence (e.g., 1 hundred, 3 tens, and 7 ones equals 1 hundred, 2 tens, and 17 ones or 13 tens and 7 ones)

◆ Reading and writing 2- and 3-digit numbers

◆ Adding multiples of 10 to, and subtracting multiples of 10 from, 2-digit numbers

More or Less?

Students use estimation to determine whether the sum of an addition problem they see displayed for a brief time is "more or less than 100 (or $1.00)". They share their estimates, and describe their thinking.

Math Focus Points

◆ Breaking apart, reordering, or combining numbers within a problem for easier computation

◆ Using knowledge of place value and known combinations to estimate sums

◆ Practicing addition skills

Practice and Review

IN THIS UNIT

Practice and review play a critical role in the *Investigations* program. The following components and features are available to provide regular reinforcement of key mathematical concepts and procedures.

Books	Features	In This Unit ...
Curriculum Unit	**The Classroom Routines** and **Ten-Minute Math** activities, to be done in ten minutes outside of math class, are introduced in a unit and repeated throughout the grade. Specific directions for the day's activity are provided in each session. For the full description and variations of the Classroom Routines and Ten-Minute Math activities, see *Implementing Investigations in Grade 3*.	• **All sessions**
Student Activity Book	**Daily Practice** pages in the *Student Activity Book* provide one of three types of written practice: **reinforcement** of the content of the unit, **ongoing review,** or **enrichment** opportunities. Some Daily Practice pages will also have Ongoing Review items with multiple-choice problems similar to those on standardized tests.	• **All sessions**
	Homework pages in the *Student Activity Book* are an extension of the work done in class. At times they help students prepare for upcoming activities.	• **Session 1.1** • **Session 2.1** • **Session 1.2** • **Session 2.3** • **Session 1.4** • **Session 2.4** • **Session 1.6** • **Session 2.6** • **Session 1.8** • **Session 2.7**
Student Math Handbook	**Math Words and Ideas** in the *Student Math Handbook* are pages that summarize key words and ideas. Most Words and Ideas pages have at least one exercise.	• **Student Math Handbook, pp. 6–24, 29–30, 36–38**
	Games pages are found in a section of the *Student Math Handbook*.	• **Student Math Handbook, pp. G3, G5, G6, G16**

Supporting the Range of Learners

The **Differentiation and Intervention Guide** provides Intervention, Extension, and Practice activities for use within each Investigation.

Sessions	1.1	1.2	1.4	1.5	1.6	1.8	2.1	2.2	2.3	2.4	2.5	2.6	2.7	2.8
Intervention	•	•	•	•	•	•	•	•		•	•	•	•	•
Extension	•					•						•		
ELL		•			•	•	•	•	•					

Intervention

Suggestions are made to support students who are having difficulty with a particular idea, activity, or problem.

Extension

Suggestions are made to support and engage students who finish early or may be ready for additional challenge.

English Language Learners (ELL)

This unit offers many opportunities for English Language Learners to practice computation skills. You can emphasize the relevant vocabulary through modeling, small group discussions, and previewing instructions. Since English Language Learners may not fully understand class discussions about strategies such as "adding by place," you can work with them individually or in small groups to clarify such ideas.

Many sessions in this unit center on class discussions about strategies for solving story problems, which may be difficult for English Language Learners to follow. In smaller groups, you can teach English Language Learners the necessary vocabulary. They will need to understand and be able to use present and past tense forms of verbs such as *buy, give (away),* and *have,* as well as math-related terms such as *add, more, plus, equals* and *equation.* Demonstrating the actions as you say the words will help English Language Learners learn this vocabulary. You might make statements such as

the following: "You *had* three strips of ten stickers. I *gave* you 20 *more* stickers. How many stickers do you *have* now?"

To help English Language Learners express their own strategies, you can point to their equations while you say what you see. Emphasize key sequence words such as *first, next, then,* and *last:* "I see that you *added* 22 + 79 and got very *close* to 100. You *made* 101. It looks like you *first* added the *ones*—9 plus 2—to *make* 11. *Next* you *traded* 10 ones for 1 ten. *Then* you added the *tens*—2 plus 7 plus the one you traded—to *make* 10. So you have 10 *tens* and 1 *one,* which *equals* 101." As English Language Learners feel comfortable using this vocabulary, you can ask them to share their strategies with you individually or in a small group. Over time, they will become more confident about sharing with the whole class.

Working with the Range of Learners: Classroom Cases is a set of episodes written by teachers that focuses on meeting the needs of the range of learners in the classroom. In the first section, *Setting up the Mathematical Community,* teachers write about how they create a supportive and productive learning environment in their classrooms. In the next section, *Accommodations for Learning,* teachers focus on specific modifications they make to meet the needs of some of their learners. In the last section, *Language and Representation,* teachers share how they help students use representations and develop language to investigate and express mathematical ideas. The questions at the end of each case provide a starting point for your own reflection or for discussion with colleagues. See *Implementing Investigations in Grade 3* for this set of episodes.

Mathematical Emphases

The Base-Ten Number System Understanding the equivalence of one group and the units that comprise it

Math Focus Points

◆ Recognizing and representing the place value of each digit in 2- and 3-digit numbers

◆ Using equivalencies among pennies, dimes, and dollars

◆ Finding different combinations of 100s, 10s, and 1s for a number, and recognizing their equivalence (i.e. 1 hundred, 3 tens, and 7 ones equals 1 hundred, 2 tens, and 17 ones, or 13 tens and 7 ones)

◆ Recognizing and demonstrating the equivalence of one 100 to ten 10s and of one 10 and ten 1s

Computational Fluency Adding and subtracting accurately and efficiently

Math Focus Points

◆ Adding and subtracting multiples of 10

◆ Solving addition problems with 2-digit numbers by using strategies that involve breaking numbers apart by place or adding one number in parts

◆ Solving addition problems with 2-digit numbers that involve more than 10 ones in the ones place and explaining the effect on the sum

◆ Finding the difference between a 2-digit number and 100

◆ Adding pennies and dimes to sums up to $2.00

Hundreds, Tens, and Ones

	Student Activity Book	Student Math Handbook	Professional Development: Read Ahead of Time	
SESSION 1.1 p. 26				
Stickers: A Base-Ten Model Students are introduced to sticker problems as a context for representing the place value of 2- and 3-digit numbers. They represent and solve problems that involve adding and subtracting groups of 10.	1–7	6, 7–8	• **Mathematics in This Unit**, p. 10 • **Algebra Connections in This Unit**, p. 16 • **Part 4: Ten-Minute Math and Classroom Routines:** *Implementing Investigations in Grade 3:* What's the Temperature? • **Part 4: Ten-Minute Math and Classroom Routines:** *Implementing Investigations in Grade 3:* Practicing Place Value • **Teacher Note:** Place Value, p. 143 • **Teacher Note:** Stickers: A Context for Place Value, p. 145 • **Part 5: Technology in *Investigations*:** *Implementing Investigations in Grade 3:* Using Calculators with the Curriculum	
SESSION 1.2 p. 36				
Adding and Subtracting 2-Digit Numbers Students discuss representations for adding and subtracting multiples of 10. They solve a set of problems that involve adding and subtracting 2-digit numbers.	9–12	6, 12–15, 30, 36	• **Dialogue Box:** Adding 10s, p. 170 • **Teacher Note:** Mathematical Representations for Addition and Subtraction, p. 147 • **Teacher Note:** Addition Strategies, p. 149	
SESSION 1.3 p. 44				
More Than Ten Ones Students discuss addition strategies. They solve problems, including some that involve ones digits with sums greater than 10. They discuss how this affects the tens digit in the sum.	13–14	12–14	• **Teacher Note:** Does Order Matter in Addition?, p. 152	
SESSION 1.4 p. 52				
How Many More Stickers to Get 100? Students solve missing addend problems in which they find the difference between 2-digit numbers and 100. They use 100 grids and number lines as tools for solving the problems and representing their strategies.	15–18	29–30		

Classroom Routines and Ten-Minute Math

See page 18 for an overview.

What's the Temperature?
- Thermometer, temperature chart, and temperature graph, prepared as specified for Session 1.1 below.

Practicing Place Value
- T1, *Practicing Place Value* 🖥 Cut apart the images.
- Cubes, organized in towers of 10 (10 towers per pair)

Materials to Gather	Materials to Prepare
• **Cubes, organized in towers of 10** (10 towers per pair)	• **M4, 100 Chart** Make copies. (1 per student, plus extras) • **T2, Stickers: Strips and Singles** 🖥 Cut apart into individual strips and singles. • **Class pocket 100 chart** Post this chart where all students can see and reach it. • **Sticker chart** Divide chart paper into five columns, and label them "Picture," "Strips of 10," "Singles," "# Stickers," and "Equation." See page 29. • **Outdoor thermometer** Mount outside a window where it can be read. • **Temperature chart** Divide chart paper into three columns, and label them "Date," "Temperature, Celsius," and "Temperature, Fahrenheit." Label the rows with dates for each Wednesday of the school year. Include vacation weeks. See page 34. • **Temperature graph** Use chart paper to prepare a wall graph. Label the vertical axis "Temperature, Fahrenheit" and extend the scale from −10° to 100° (or further, depending on your climate). Label the horizontal axis "Date," and mark it with dates for each Wednesday of the school year. You might use colored background paper to indicate temperature ranges (red and yellow for warmer, green and blue for cooler). See page 34. • **M5–M6, Family Letter** Make copies. (1 per student)
• **M4, 100 Chart** (as needed; from Session 1.1) • **Cubes, organized in towers of 10** (10 towers per pair)	• **M7–M8, Family Letter** Make copies. (1 per student)
• **Cubes, organized in towers of 10** (10 towers per pair)	• **M9–M10, Family Letter** Make copies. (1 per student) • **Class number line** Post the class number line where all students can see it.
• **M4, 100 Chart** (as needed; from Session 1.1) • **T4, Sticker Book** 🖥	• **M12, 100 Grids** Make copies. (2 per student, plus extras)

🖥 Overhead Transparency

Hundreds, Tens, and Ones,
continued

	Student Activity Book	Student Math Handbook	Professional Development: Read Ahead of Time
SESSION 1.5 p. 60			
Capture 5: Adding and Subtracting 10s and 1s Students play *Capture 5,* a game that provides practice in adding and subtracting 10s and 1s.	19–20	G3	
SESSION 1.6 p. 65			
Assessment: Adding and Subtracting 10s Students play *Collect $2.00,* a game in which they collect a total of $2.00 in pennies, dimes, and dollars. Math Workshop focuses on finding the difference between 2-digit numbers and 100, and adding and subtracting 10s and 1s.	21–25	36, 37–38; G6	• **Part 2: Using** *Investigations*: *Implementing Investigations in Grade 3*
SESSION 1.7 p. 71			
Strategies for Capture 5 Students discuss strategies for *Capture 5.* Math Workshop continues to focus on adding and subtracting 10s and 1s and finding the difference between a number and 100 or 200.	27–30	36–38; G3	• **Dialogue Box:** Strategies for *Capture 5,* p. 171
SESSION 1.8 p. 76			
Making Numbers with 100s, 10s, and 1s Students use the sticker context to represent 3-digit numbers. They discuss equivalent combinations of stickers.	31–34	7–8, 9	
SESSION 1.9 p. 85			
Assessment: Hundreds, Tens, and Ones Students demonstrate the equivalence of 1 dollar to 10 dimes and 1 dime to 10 pennies. They are assessed on finding the difference between a 2-digit number and 100 and on representing a 2-digit number with equivalent combinations of tens and ones.	35	7–8, 37–38	• **Teacher Note:** Assessment: Hundreds, Tens, and Ones, p. 153

Materials to Gather	Materials to Prepare
• **T3, 100 Chart** 📺 • **T5, *Capture 5* Recording Sheet** 📺 • **Overhead colored chips** (12 per pair) • **Game pieces** (1 per student) • **Class pocket 100 chart with colored transparent inserts** (optional)	• **M4, 100 Chart** Make copies. (1 per pair or team of 4, plus extras) • **M13, *Capture 5*** Make copies. (as needed) Play a few rounds to familiarize yourself with the rules of the game. • **M14–M15, Change Cards** Make copies. Cut apart the cards. (1 deck per pair) • **M16, *Capture 5* Recording Sheet** Make copies. (as needed)
• **Materials for *Capture 5*** See Session 1.5 • **T6, 200 Chart** 📺 • **T7, *Collect $2.00* Recording Sheet** 📺 • **Change cards** • **Number cubes 1–6 and 7–12** (1 set per pair); **overhead colored chips; game pieces**	• **M17, *Collect $2.00*** Make copies. (as needed) • **M3, Assessment Checklist: Adding and Subtracting 10s** ✅ Make 2 copies (or as needed) to record students' progress throughout the unit. • **Pennies, Dimes, and Dollars Set** Prepare sets of 30 pennies, 20 dimes, and 4 one-dollar bills. (5 sets) • **M18, 200 Chart** Make copies. (1 per pair, plus extras) • **M19 *Collect $2.00* Recording Sheet** Make copies. (as needed)
• **T3, 100 Chart** 📺 • **M3, Assessment Checklist: Adding and Subtracting 10s** ✅ (from Session 1.6) • **Materials for *Capture 5*** See Session 1.5 • **Cubes, in towers of 10** (as needed) • **Materials for *Collect $2.00*** See Session 1.6	
• **Cubes, in towers of 10** (as needed)	• **T8, Sticker Station: Sheets** 📺 Cut out sheet and place with strips and singles from T2. • **Chart: "Ways to Make 137"** Position chart paper horizontally and divide into four columns. Label the columns "Picture," "Sheets, Strips, and Singles," "Hundreds, Tens, and Ones," and "Equation." See page 81.
• **Cubes, in towers of 10** (as needed) • **Pennies, Dimes, and Dollars Sets** (as needed; from Session 1.6)	• **M12, 100 Grids; M18, 200 Chart** Make copies. (as needed) • **M21–M22 Assessment: Hundreds, Tens, and Ones** Make copies. (1 per student) • **Chart paper** Write the following problem on chart paper or on the board: "Max is playing *Collect $2.00*, but he keeps forgetting to trade his coins. He has 13 dimes and 23 pennies. How much money does he have?"

📺 Overhead Transparency   ✅ Checklist Available

Stickers: A Base-Ten Model

Math Focus Points

◆ Recognizing and representing the place value of each digit in 2- and 3-digit numbers

◆ Adding and subtracting multiples of 10

Vocabulary

digit	Fahrenheit
sum	Celsius
degree	

Today's Plan | Materials

① ACTIVITY **Introducing Place Value: Stickers and Cubes** 20 MIN · CLASS · PAIRS		• T2* • Cubes, in towers of 10; sticker chart*; class pocket 100 chart*
② ACTIVITY **Adding and Subtracting 10s Problems** 30 MIN · INDIVIDUALS · PAIRS		• *Student Activity Book,* pp. 1–4 • M4* • Cubes, in towers of 10
③ ACTIVITY **Introducing *What's the Temperature?*** 10 MIN · CLASS		• Outdoor thermometer*; temperature chart*; temperature graph*
④ SESSION FOLLOW-UP **Daily Practice and Homework**		• *Student Activity Book,* pp. 5–7 • *Student Math Handbook,* pp. 6, 7–8 • M5–M6, Family Letter*

*See *Materials to Prepare,* p. 23.

Ten-Minute Math

Note: The Ten-Minute Math activity for this unit, *Practicing Place Value,* is introduced in this session. Plan to do today's Ten-Minute Math sometime after math class, if possible.

Practicing Place Value: Stickers and Cubes   Write the number 39 on the board and ask students to say it to a partner. Make sure all students can read, write, and say this number correctly. Then, ask students to represent the number using cubes.

• How many towers of 10 and single cubes did you use?

• How many cubes will you have if you add one more tower of 10 to this representation?

• If you add two more towers?

• How about if you subtract two towers of 10?

If time remains, pose similar problems using the number 51.

ACTIVITY

1 Introducing Place Value: Stickers and Cubes

20 MIN · CLASS · PAIRS

This activity uses stickers and cubes to help students understand place value.❶ ❷ In addition, the activity introduces the Ten-Minute Math activity *Practicing Place Value,* which students will continue to do throughout this unit and at other times during the school year.❸

Distribute 100 cubes in towers of 10 to each pair of students.

For the next few weeks, we will be working on addition and subtraction. We'll use some different tools, such as stickers, 100 charts, and number lines.❹

Most of you probably remember Sticker Station from Grade 2. Sticker Station is a very popular store that sells all kinds of stickers. To keep things organized, and to make buying stickers easier, Sticker Station sells stickers in different ways. You can buy individual stickers called "singles," or you can buy strips of stickers.

On the overhead, show a few transparent singles and strips that you have prepared from Stickers: Strips and Singles (T2).

What do you notice about the way these stickers are organized? How many stickers do you get on a strip? How many singles is that equal to?

Establish that there are 10 stickers on a strip and that 10 singles are equivalent to one strip of 10. Then use the transparent stickers to pose a few problems.

Display four strips of 10 and 6 singles.

Professional Development

❶ **Teacher Note:** Place Value, p. 143

❷ **Teacher Note:** Stickers: A Context for Place Value, p. 145

❸ **Part 4: Ten-Minute Math and Classroom Routines:** *Implementing Investigations in Grade 3:* Practicing Place Value

Math Note

❹ **Math Tools** Number lines and 100 charts are useful tools for understanding and representing the operations of addition and subtraction. Students worked with both of these tools in Grade 2. Throughout this unit and for the remainder of the year, post a class number line and 100 chart in visible places in the classroom.

Trading Stickers, Combining Coins

Stickers: Strips and Singles

T2

▲ Transparencies, T2

Teaching Notes

⑤ Strips of 10 As frequently as possible, refer to strips as *strips of 10* to reinforce the groupings of 10s and 1s.

⑥ Using Shorthand Because it can be challenging for students to draw towers of 10 cubes, and time-consuming as the numbers get larger, suggest a shorthand method of representing the stickers. For example, use lines, sticks, or tall rectangles to represent towers of 10 and dots or very small squares for singles. Model this method when you draw in the first column of the chart.

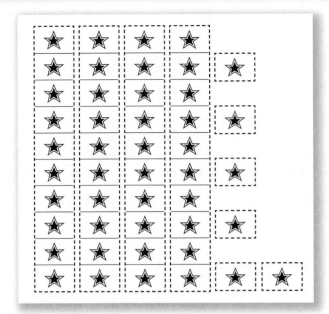

Suppose that Pilar went to Sticker Station, and this is what she bought. How many strips of 10 did she buy?⑤ How many singles? How many stickers did she buy altogether? How do you know?

Students might say:

"I can count by 10s to get 40. Then I count on by 1s to get 6. I know that 40 and 6 is 46."

"There's a group of 40, and a group of 6, and I know that 40 plus 6 equals 46."

As students describe their thinking, point to the transparent stickers to support their ideas. Then record the stickers Pilar bought. Use pictures, numbers, and words on the sticker chart you prepared and posted ahead of time.⑥ Also record the numbers of stickers in strips and singles as an equation, $40 + 6 = 46$, in the last column of the chart.

Picture	Strips of 10	Singles	# Stickers	Equation
‖‖‖‖ ⋮⋮	4 strips	6 singles	46 stickers	40 + 6 = 46

Suppose that Pilar went to Sticker Station again and bought another strip of 10 stickers. Use your cubes to show what that would look like.

Ask a pair of students to show the new amount on the overhead. Count by 10s together as a class to reinforce that 5 groups of 10 is equal to 50. Ask how many stickers the towers of 10 and single cubes represent altogether, and how you could write that as an equation (50 + 6 = 56). On the chart, record how many stickers Pilar has now, filling each column.

So Pilar now has 56 stickers. Suppose that she went back to Sticker Station the next day and bought one more strip of 10. How many stickers would that be? Show that amount with cubes.

Have a second pair of students show that amount in cubes. Ask again how many stickers the cubes represent and what equation represents the amount. Then record the amounts and equation on the chart.

Now Pilar has 66 stickers. Suppose that she went to Sticker Station a week later and bought two more strips of 10. How many stickers would she have then? Show the total amount with cubes.

Cubes in towers of 10 and singles are a good model for adding 10s.

Repeat the procedure above for 86 stickers. Then direct students' attention to the numbers of stickers in the fourth column: 46, 56, 66, and 86.

Picture	Strips of 10	Singles	# Stickers	Equation
	4 strips	6 singles	46 stickers	40 + 6 = 46
	5 strips	6 singles	56 stickers	50 + 6 = 56
	6 strips	6 singles	66 stickers	60 + 6 = 66
	8 strips	6 singles	86 stickers	80 + 6 = 86

What **digit** changed every time Pilar bought more strips of 10? How did it change?

Students may notice that the digit in the 10s place increases by 1 each time another 10 is added and increases by 2 when two 10s are added. Use the class pocket 100 chart to help students understand that the 1 and 2 represent 10 and 20 being added to the starting number of stickers.

Ask a student to locate the number 46 on the 100 chart. Show the result of adding first one strip of 10, then another strip of 10, and then two more strips of 10. If the student jumps down the column from 46 to 86, ask which spaces on the 100 chart represent the strips of 10 and 20 stickers added.

41	42	43	44	45	46	47	48	49	50
51	52	53	54	55	56	57	58	59	60
61	62	63	64	65	66	67	68	69	70
71	72	73	74	75	76	77	78	79	80
81	82	83	84	85	86	87	88	89	90
91	92	93	94	95	96	97	98	99	100

You showed that 46 plus 10 equals 56. What sum did we get when we added 56 and 10? What about 66 and 20?

As students respond, write the following equations on the board:

$$46 + 10 = 56$$

$$56 + 10 = 66$$

$$66 + 20 = 86$$

▲ **Resource Masters, M4; T3**

Teaching Note

❼ **Adding and Subtracting Mutilples of 10** The ability to add and subtract multiples of 10 is a benchmark of this unit. During this and the next five sessions, observe students informally to assess the progress they are making toward meeting this benchmark. This benchmark is assessed in Sessions 1.6 and 1.7 during Math Workshop. A checklist (M3) is provided to record your observations.

ACTIVITY

30 MIN   INDIVIDUALS   PAIRS

② Adding and Subtracting 10s Problems

Students solve some problems about adding and subtracting multiples of 10. Direct their attention to the first problem on *Student Activity Book* page 1, and solve it together.❼

How many stickers does Tori have? What about Joel? If they put their stickers together, how many will there be?

Remind students that they can use sketches of stickers, cubes, and the 100 chart to help them solve the problem. Make copies of the 100 Chart (M4) available. When students are ready, ask for volunteers to explain

Technology Note

8 Using Calculators in This Unit For the activities in this unit, students should not be using calculators. The work supports students as they develop mental and pencil-and-paper strategies for solving addition and subtraction problems. Focus should be on reasoning about adding and subtracting multiples of 10 and on breaking numbers apart for easier calculation. Nonetheless, students should become familiar with calculators and how to use them effectively. Read **Part 5: Technology in** *Investigations:* Using Calculators with the Curriculum in *Implementing Investigations in Grade 3.*

Name _____ Date _____

Trading Stickers, Combining Coins

Problems for Adding and Subtracting 10s (page 1 of 4)

1. Tori's stickers   Joel's stickers

Number of stickers: _____ | Number of stickers: _____

If Tori and Joel put their stickers together, how many stickers will they have in all? Write an equation that represents the problem.

Equation: _____

Session 1.1   Unit 1 ①

▲ **Student Activity Book, pp. 1–2**

---

their solutions. Encourage them to use cubes or sketches to demonstrate their thinking. Then ask how they determined the total number of stickers.

Students continue working on *Student Activity Book* pages 1–4.**8**

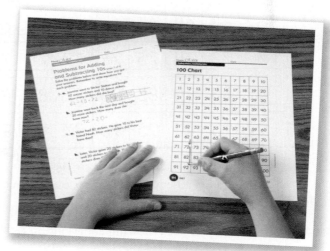

Students might use the 100 chart to help them solve these problems.

ONGOING ASSESSMENT: Observing Students at Work

Students solve problems in which they add and subtract multiples of 10 to and from 2-digit numbers.

- **How do students determine the number of stickers for each person in problems 1, 2, and 7?** Do they count by 10s? Do they see three 10s as 30, four 10s as 40, and so on?

- **How do they determine the total number of stickers in the first two problems?** Do they add 30 and 30 mentally? Do they count up by 10s from the first number?

- **Do students use tools such as cubes, sketches of stickers, or the 100 chart to add or subtract 10s?**

DIFFERENTIATION: Supporting the Range of Learners

Intervention If students are having trouble solving the problems, determine first whether they can represent a number with cubes. For those who are still having difficulty, ask questions such as the following:

- In this problem you are adding 27 and 10. Can you use cubes to show me what 27 looks like? If you add another stick of 10 (or strip of stickers), what number will you have? Can you find the number 27 on the 100 chart? Show what happens when you add 10 to that number.

Extension Some students will understand the result of adding and subtracting 10s without using place value materials. Challenge these students by asking them to add larger multiples of 10.

- In Problem 3, you figured out that Jasmine now has 92 stickers. How many stickers will she have if she buys five more strips of 10? How many will she have if she adds seven strips of 10 to her 92 stickers?

ACTIVITY

③ Introducing *What's the Temperature?*

10 MIN   CLASS

What's the Temperature? is a routine in which the class reads an outdoor thermometer every Wednesday morning and records the temperature, in degrees, on a chart and on a graph. Through this routine, students learn how to read a thermometer and develop a sense of what different temperatures feel like (on the Fahrenheit and Celsius scales). In addition, students become familiar with charts and graphs and the relationships between them. ⑨ ⑩

Briefly explain the routine and display the temperature chart and graph. Send a student to read the thermometer and report the temperature to the class. If this is a Wednesday, fill in the chart with a marker. Otherwise, just use pencil to demonstrate.

Professional Development

⑨ **Part 4: Ten-Minute Math and Classroom Routines:** *Implementing Investigations in Grade 3: What's the Temperature?*

Teaching Note

⑩ **The Temperature Routine** It is very important to fill in the temperature graph from the beginning of the year because this routine lays the groundwork for the first Investigation in the unit *Stories, Tables, and Graphs*. In that Investigation, students will look at the information they have recorded all year. They will compare their class data with data collected in cities around the world.

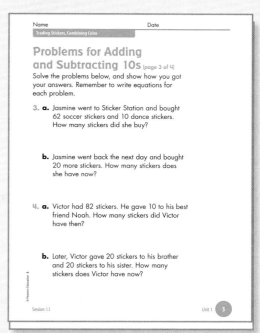

Name _____ Date _____

Trading Stickers, Combining Coins

Problems for Adding and Subtracting 10s (page 3 of 4)

Solve the problems below, and show how you got your answers. Remember to write equations for each problem.

3. **a.** Jasmine went to Sticker Station and bought 62 soccer stickers and 10 dance stickers. How many stickers did she buy?

   b. Jasmine went back the next day and bought 20 more stickers. How many stickers does she have now?

4. **a.** Victor had 82 stickers. He gave 10 to his best friend Noah. How many stickers did Victor have then?

   b. Later, Victor gave 20 stickers to his brother and 20 stickers to his sister. How many stickers does Victor have now?

Session 1.1   Unit 1 ③

▲ **Student Activity Book, pp. 3–4**

Date	Temperature/ Fahrenheit	Temperature/ Celsius
September 8	72 degrees	22 degrees
September 15		
September 22		
September 29		

Next, record the temperature on the graph in marker (if Wednesday) or pencil. Help students understand how the dot you place on the chart relates to the values on the horizontal and vertical axes.

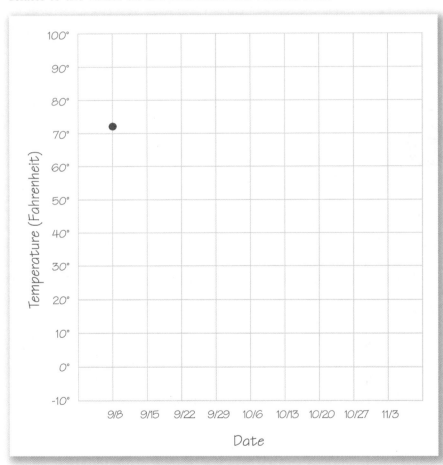

SESSION FOLLOW-UP

④ Daily Practice and Homework

 Daily Practice: For reinforcement of this unit's content, have students complete *Student Activity Book* page 5.

 Homework: Ask students to complete *Student Activity Book* pages 6–7, writing the numbers represented by stickers and drawing stickers to represent given numbers.

 Student Math Handbook: Students and families may use *Student Math Handbook* pages 6, 7–8 for reference and review. See pages 174–181 in the back of this unit.

 Family Letter: Send home copies of the Family Letter (M5–M6).

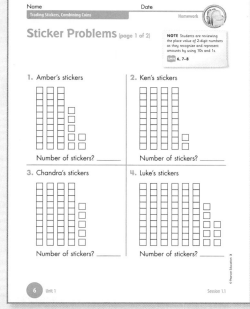

▲ **Student Activity Book, p. 6**

Name _____ Date _____
Trading Stickers, Combining Coins   Daily Practice

How Many Stickers?

NOTE Students practice representing 2-digit numbers using the sticker context.
SMH 6, 7–8

1. Julia's stickers
_____ stickers

2. Quinn's stickers
_____ stickers

3. Erika's stickers
_____ stickers

4. Cody's stickers
_____ stickers

Ongoing Review

5. Find the missing number: 160, 260, 360, 460, _____

   A. 860   **B.** 560   **C.** 500   **D.** 480

Session 1.1   Unit 1   5

▲ **Student Activity Book, p. 5**

Name _____ Date _____
Trading Stickers, Combining Coins   Homework

Sticker Problems (page 2 of 2)

5. Show 37 stickers. Use strips of 10 and singles.

6. Show 51 stickers. Use strips of 10 and singles.

Session 1.1   Unit 1   7

▲ **Student Activity Book, p. 7**

Adding and Subtracting 2-Digit Numbers

Math Focus Points

◆ Recognizing and representing the place value of each digit in 2- and 3-digit numbers

◆ Adding and subtracting multiples of 10

◆ Solving addition problems with 2-digit numbers by using strategies that involve breaking numbers apart by place or adding one number in parts

Vocabulary

equation
tens place
ones place
difference

Today's Plan		Materials
DISCUSSION **①** **Representations of Adding and Subtracting 10s**	20 MIN CLASS	• Cubes, in towers of 10; class pocket 100 chart
ACTIVITY **②** **Adding and Subtracting 10s and 1s**	40 MIN INDIVIDUALS PAIRS	• *Student Activity Book,* pp. 9–10 • M4 (from Session 1.1) • Cubes, in towers of 10
SESSION FOLLOW-UP **③** **Daily Practice and Homework**		• *Student Activity Book,* pp. 11–12 • *Student Math Handbook,* pp. 6, 12–15, 29–30, 36 • M4 (from Session 1.1); M7–M8, Family Letter*

*See *Materials to Prepare,* p. 23.

Ten-Minute Math

Practicing Place Value: Stickers and Cubes Show Image 1 from *Practicing Place Value* (T1), for 5 to 8 seconds. Students write the number and represent it using cubes. Show the image once more to make any revisions.

• What number does the image represent?

• How many towers of ten and single cubes did you use?

Repeat the process with Image 2. Once students have represented both numbers with cubes, ask:

• What is the relationship between the two images?

DISCUSSION

Representing Adding and Subtracting 10s

20 MIN **CLASS**

Math Focus Points for Discussion

◆ Recognizing and representing the place value of each digit in 2- and 3-digit numbers

◆ Adding and subtracting multiples of 10

Distribute 100 cubes in towers of 10 to each pair of students.

Have students refer to Problem 5 on *Student Activity Book* page 4 as you write it on the board.

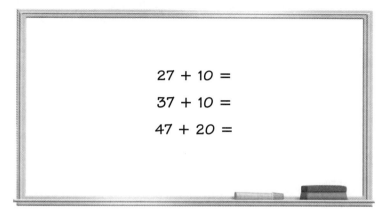

$$27 + 10 =$$
$$37 + 10 =$$
$$47 + 20 =$$

When you worked on the first **equation**, what number did you add to 27? What sum did you get?❶

Ask a student to show $27 + 10$ on the class 100 chart. If the student moves directly down to 37, ask him or her to prove that the move was 10 spaces. This will help students who are less sure of the vertical move to clearly see the 10 that was added. Write 37 next to the first equation. To provide a second way of visualizing the problem, ask a different student to represent the equation with cubes.❷ ❸

I noticed that some of you used cubes to represent the starting number in the equation. How many towers of 10 did you use to start? How many single cubes? What did you do when you had to add 10? How many towers of 10 did you have then? How many singles?

Let's look at the second equation. What's happening here? Can you show that move on the 100 chart? What number do you land on this time?

Trading Stickers, Combining Coins

Practicing Place Value

Image 1 | Image 2

Image 3 | Image 4

T1

▲ Transparencies, T1

Once again, have one student show the equation on the 100 chart and have a second student demonstrate with cubes.

A student uses the 100 chart to show 27 + 10.

Both times that we added 10 to the starting number in the equation, we ended up in the space right under that number. Does this happen every time you add 10 to a number on the 100 chart? Can you explain why?

Students might say:

 "We're adding a 10 and not adding any 1s, so only the tens place changes."

In the third equation, we are adding 20 to 47. Can someone show that on the 100 chart? Can someone show that with cubes?❹

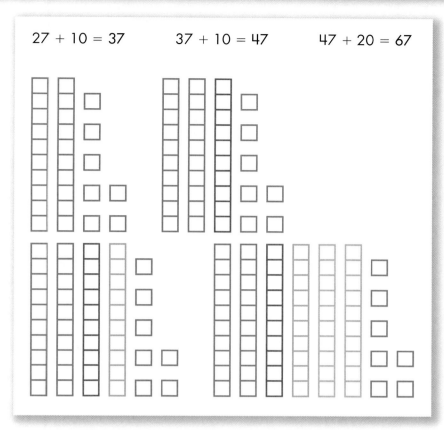

To examine what happens when 10s are subtracted from a number, discuss Problem 6. Repeat the procedure above, again asking students to model these equations on the 100 chart and with cubes.

You noticed before that when you added 10 or 20 to a number, the sum had a different digit in the tens place, but the same digit in the ones place. What happened when you subtracted 10 or 20? How did the difference—the number you ended up with when you subtracted—compare with the number you started with?

Ask students to compare 78, the starting number, with 68. What changed when 10 was subtracted? What happened when another 10 was subtracted, and then when 20 was subtracted? Listen for explanations that focus on how subtracting exactly 10 or a multiple of 10 affects the number of tens (represented by the tens digit in the difference), while the number of ones (represented by the ones digit in the difference) is the same as the ones digit in the original amount.

Some of you said that the tens place is increasing (or decreasing) by one. I see what you mean. This [pointing] goes from 2 to 3 to 4 (or from 7 to 6 to 5), but is this really "1" that the number is increasing (or decreasing) by?

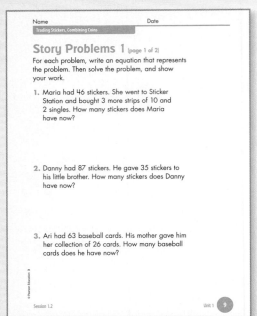

Name _____ Date _____

Trading Stickers, Combining Coins

Story Problems 1 (page 1 of 2)

For each problem, write an equation that represents the problem. Then solve the problem, and show your work.

1. Maria had 46 stickers. She went to Sticker Station and bought 3 more strips of 10 and 2 singles. How many stickers does Maria have now?

2. Danny had 87 stickers. He gave 35 stickers to his little brother. How many stickers does Danny have now?

3. Ari had 63 baseball cards. His mother gave him her collection of 26 cards. How many baseball cards does he have now?

Session 1.2   Unit 1   9

▲ **Student Activity Book, p. 9**

Name _____ Date _____

Trading Stickers, Combining Coins

Story Problems 1 (page 2 of 2)

4. Ms. Ruiz's students baked 75 muffins for the bake sale. They sold 53. How many muffins did they have left?

5. Alex had 72 stickers. He went to Sticker Station and bought 4 strips of 10 and 7 singles. How many stickers does he have now?

6. Deonte counted 47 squirrels on Saturday at the park. He went back on Sunday and counted 42 more. How many squirrels did he count in all?

10   Unit 1   Session 1.2

▲ **Student Activity Book, p. 10**

ACTIVITY

2 Adding and Subtracting 10s and 1s

40 MIN INDIVIDUALS PAIRS

Write Problem 1 on the board from *Student Activity Book*, page 9 and ask a student to read it aloud:

> Maria had 46 stickers. She went to Sticker Station and bought 3 more strips of 10 and 2 singles. How many stickers does Maria have now?

We just looked at what happens when 10, or a multiple of 10 such as 20 or 30, is added to or subtracted from a number. Now you're going to work on problems that involve adding and subtracting both 10s and 1s, like this problem about Maria. How many stickers did Maria start with? How many more stickers did she buy? What equation represents this problem?

Students are likely to suggest $46 + 32 =$ _____ or $46 + 30 + 2 =$ _____. Write these equations on the board below the problem.

Work with a person sitting near you to solve this problem. What tools can you use to help you?

Give students a few minutes to solve the problem. Then call them back together to share strategies. Keep this sharing time brief, because students will start the next session with a longer discussion about their strategies.

Students are likely to have solved the problem with different strategies, including adding by place or adding one number in parts.❺ ❻

Did anyone start by adding 40 + 30? What did you do next? Did you use cubes or stickers to help you solve the problem?

Call on a student who used this strategy. Model how to record each step using equations, vertical notation, and a sketch of the sticker place value model.❼ ❽

$40 + 30 = 70$

$6 + 2 = 8$

$70 + 8 = 78$

$$\begin{array}{r} 46 \\ + 32 \\ \hline 70 \quad (40 + 30) \\ 8 \quad (6 + 2) \\ \hline 78 \quad (70 + 8) \end{array}$$

Did anyone start with 46 and add on parts of 32? How did you start? What did you do next? What tools did you use to help you?

Call on a student who used this strategy, and again model how to record each step the student used.

$46 + 10 = 56$ -or- $46 + 30 = 76$

$56 + 10 = 66$ $76 + 2 = 78$

$66 + 10 = 76$

$76 + 2 = 78$

For the remainder of this session, students work individually or in pairs to solve the problems on *Student Activity Book* pages 9–10. Remind them to record the steps they use to solve each problem.

Professional Development

❺ **Teacher Note:** Addition Strategies, p. 149

Math Note

❻ **Notation** Students should see both vertical and horizontal notation for recording the steps to solutions to computation problems. Some students may come to your class already believing that when they see a problem written in the vertical form, they must carry out a particular algorithm, rather than consider what they know about the numbers in the problem. Instead, students should see both kinds of notation as an efficient way to record a problem and its solution.

Algebra Notes

❼ **Order Doesn't Matter** All the strategies in this discussion involve breaking apart one or both addends and combining the parts in a different order. See the algebra essay, page 16, for more information.

❽ **Representing Operations** Using models to represent the actions of the operations (for example, removing or crossing out for subtraction) not only supports computation but also provides tools for reasoning about the generalizations that underlie the computation.

Teaching Note

⑨ **Place Value Sketches** Continue to model line-and-dot sketches for the sticker place value representation. Examples in this unit generally organize the single dots in columns of five to help students visualize quantities less than 10. Students need not follow this convention, but should learn to keep their sketches very simple whenever they record strategies with the sticker model.

ONGOING ASSESSMENT: Observing Students at Work

Students solve problems that involve adding and subtracting 2-digit numbers.

- **Can students write equations that accurately represent the problems?**

- **Do they use tools to solve these problems and/or represent their strategies?**

- **What addition strategies are students using?** Do they add by place, combining the tens and ones separately, and then adding the totals? Do they add on one number in parts? If so, can they add 10 without counting by ones? Can they add a multiple of 10 without counting up by tens? Can they find a sum that is over 100?

- **How are students solving the subtraction problems?** Do they use their knowledge of subtracting 10s to subtract the second number in parts? Do they represent the first number with cubes or stickers and then "take away" the second number by removing or crossing out that number of cubes or stickers? ⑨

Look for students who are adding by place to solve the addition problems or adding on one number in parts. Ask these students to be prepared to share their strategies in the next session's discussion.

DIFFERENTIATION: Supporting the Range of Learners

Intervention If some students are still unsure about how to proceed, work with them in a small group to find and represent the solution to Problem 1. Have them begin by using cubes or sketches of stickers to model the action of the problem. If students are still having difficulty, consider starting with smaller amounts. For example, in Problem 2, ask these students to first add one strip of ten and to model that with cubes or sketches.

ELL Since students from other countries may have learned how to do addition differently in their native countries, you may want to do some 2-digit computations with these students in advance. Watch how they compute the problems to see the methods they have been taught. You can then use the students' strategies as points of reference when helping them see other ways of solving problems.

SESSION FOLLOW-UP

Daily Practice and Homework

 Daily Practice: For reinforcement of this unit's content, have students complete *Student Activity Book* page 11.

 Homework: Ask students to solve problems that involve adding and subtracting 10s on *Student Activity Book* page 12. Have copies of the 100 Chart (M4) available for students to take home.

 Student Math Handbook: Students and families may use *Student Math Handbook* pages 6, 12–15, 29–30, 36 for reference and review. See pages 174–181 in the back of this unit.

 Family Letter: Send home copies of the Family Letter (M7–M8).

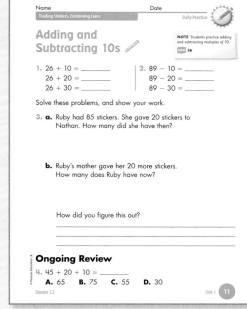

▲ **Student Activity Book, p. 11**

▲ **Student Activity Book, p. 12**

More Than Ten Ones

Math Focus Points

◆ Solving addition problems with 2-digit numbers by using strategies that involve breaking numbers apart by place or adding one number in parts

◆ Solving addition problems with 2-digit numbers that involve more than 10 ones in the ones place and explaining the effect on the sum

Vocabulary

adding by place
adding one number in parts
number line

Today's Plan		Materials
DISCUSSION **1 Story Problem Strategies**	20 MIN CLASS	• *Student Activity Book*, p. 9 (completed in Session 1.2) • Cubes, in towers of 10; class number line*
ACTIVITY **2 Addition Problems with More Than Ten Ones**	20 MIN INDIVIDUALS PAIRS	• *Student Activity Book*, pp. 13–15 • Cubes, in towers of 10
DISCUSSION **3 Ten Ones Equal One Ten**	20 MIN CLASS	• *Student Activity Book*, p. 13 • Cubes, in towers of 10
SESSION FOLLOW-UP **4 Daily Practice**		• *Student Activity Book*, p. 14 • *Student Math Handbook*, pp. 12–15 • M9–M10, Family Letter

*See *Materials to Prepare*, p. 23.

Ten-Minute Math

Practicing Place Value: Stickers and Cubes Show Image 3 from *Practicing Place Value* (T1), for 5 to 8 seconds. Students write the number and represent it using cubes. Show the image once more to make any revisions.

• What number does the image represent? How many towers of ten and single cubes did you use?

Repeat the process with Image 4. Once students have represented both numbers with cubes, ask:

• What is the relationship between the two images?

DISCUSSION

① Story Problem Strategies

20 MIN   CLASS

Math Focus Points for Discussion

◆ Solving addition problems with 2-digit numbers by using strategies that involve breaking numbers apart by place or adding one number in parts

Direct attention to Problem 3 on *Student Activity Book* page 9, and ask a student to read the problem aloud:

Ari had 63 baseball cards. His mother gave him her collection of 26 cards. How many baseball cards does he have now?

How many baseball cards did Ari have to start? How many more did his mother give him? What equation can we write to represent this problem?

Write 63 + 26 = _____ on the board. Ask a student who broke numbers apart by place to share his or her strategy.

Students might say:

"First I added 60 and 20 and got 80. Then I added the 3 and 6 and got 9. I added the 80 and 9 together and got 89."

Record the student's strategy, using equations.

$$60 + 20 = 80$$
$$3 + 6 \ = 9$$
$$80 + 9 \ = 89$$

How can we describe what Deondra did to solve this problem? What did she add first? Where did the 60 and 20 come from? What did she do next? Where did she get the 3 and 6?

After some discussion, ask a student to use cubes to show the strategy.

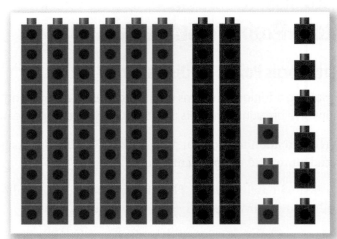

Ask students whether they remember using this strategy in Grade 2, and help them name it. For example:

You noticed that Deondra first added the tens, then she added the ones, and then she combined them. She used a strategy that some of you are calling "adding tens and ones" or "adding by place." We can also record this strategy vertically.

Write 63 + 26 vertically, and model how to record the strategy of adding by place.

$$
\begin{array}{r}
63 \\
+\ 26 \\
\hline
80 \\
+\ 9 \\
\hline
89
\end{array}
$$

First, Deondra added the tens. (60 + 20)
Then, she added the ones. (3 + 6)
Next, she added the tens to the ones. (80 + 9)

Next, ask students who added one number on in parts to share their strategy.

Students might say:

"I started with 63 and added 10 to 73 and 10 more to 83. Then I added the 6 and got 89."

"I started with 63 and added 6 to get to 69. Then I added 20 to get to 89."

Ask what equations represent each of these strategies. Record the responses.

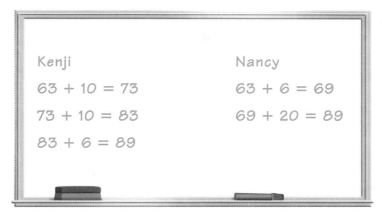

Kenji

63 + 10 = 73

73 + 10 = 83

83 + 6 = 89

Nancy

63 + 6 = 69

69 + 20 = 89

Look at these equations. Where in these equations do you see the 26 cards that Ari's mother gave him? What's alike about what Kenji and Nancy did? What's different?

Students are likely to comment on the fact that Kenji and Nancy both started with 63 and added two 10s (or the equivalent 20) and six 1s to that number. They are also likely to notice that they added these numbers in different orders.❶ Ask students whether they have a name for this strategy.

So both of these students started with one number in the equation and added the other number in parts. We can call this strategy "adding one number in parts."

Let's show what **adding one number in parts** looks like on the class number line. We'll start with Kenji. What number did he start with? What did he do next?

As students describe Kenji's moves, record them on the class number line. Then ask a volunteer to record Nancy's moves on the number line. In both cases, help students link the moves on the number line to the numbers in the original problem.❷

Professional Development

❶ **Teacher Note:** Does Order Matter in Addition?, p. 152

Teaching Note

❷ **Using Math Tools** Throughout this unit, students are encouraged to use such tools as cubes, sticker strips and singles, the number line, and the 100 chart. Have these available for students to use as needed. Some students will need these tools to solve problems, and others will primarily use them to represent and clearly communicate their strategies. Over time, many students will be able to solve familiar problems without the tools. However, models and representations help students understand the operations; they provide visual images that students can call on as they are challenged by problems with larger numbers; and they support students' reasoning about the generalizations that underlie their strategies.

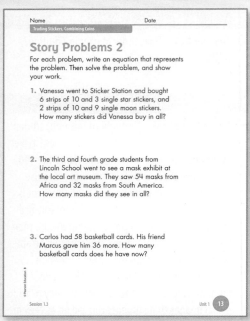

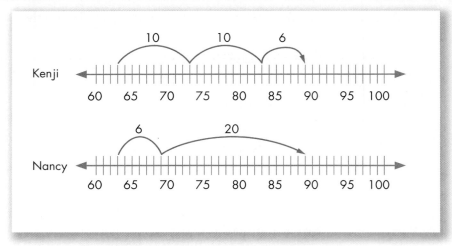

Let's look at the number line and connect it to the problem. Where does it show the number of cards that Ari started with? Where is the amount of cards that his mother gave him? How many cards did Ari end up with? Where do you see that amount on the number line?

ACTIVITY

2 Addition Problems with More Than Ten Ones

20 MIN INDIVIDUALS PAIRS

Ask a volunteer to read Problem 1 on *Student Activity Book* page 13: "Vanessa went to Sticker Station and bought 6 strips of 10 and 3 single star stickers and 2 strips of 10 and 9 single moon stickers. How many stickers did Vanessa buy in all?"

What equation represents this problem?

Write $63 + 29 =$ _____ on the board.

Do you think the answer will be in the 80s or 90s? Why do you think that? We just solved another problem, $63 + 26$. Why was the answer to that problem in the 80s?

For now, take a few initial ideas. You will return to these questions after students have worked on the problems.

For the next 20 minutes, work alone or with a partner to solve all three problems. Then we'll discuss your solutions. Pay attention to how these problems are alike and how they are different.

ONGOING ASSESSMENT: Observing Students at Work

Students solve addition problems with 2-digit numbers, some of which have ones digits with a sum greater than 10.

- **Can students write equations that accurately represent the problems?**

- **What addition strategies do students use?** Do they add by place, combining the tens or ones separately, and then add the totals? Do they add one number to the other in parts?

- **Are students able to solve the problems in which the ones digits have a sum greater than 10?**

DISCUSSION
Ten Ones Equal One Ten

20 MIN   CLASS

Math Focus Points for Discussion

◆ Solving addition problems with 2-digit numbers that involve more than 10 ones in the ones place and explaining the effect on the sum

Direct students' attention again to Problem 1 on *Student Activity Book* page 13 (63 star stickers plus 29 moon stickers).

What happened when you added the two numbers in this problem? Was your answer in the 80s, as it was in the problem about Ari's baseball cards (63 + 26)? What makes these 2 problems different? Why did you get an answer in the 80s for the first problem and an answer in the 90s for the second?

Have a few students share their answers and strategies for solving the problem. Listen for ideas about the total number of ones in each problem—how the sum of the ones is less than 10 in Ari's baseball card problem and more than 10 in Vanessa's sticker problem. To make this clear to all students, ask one student to model the first problem with cubes and another to do the same with the second problem. You might also draw these on the board with sketches of stickers.

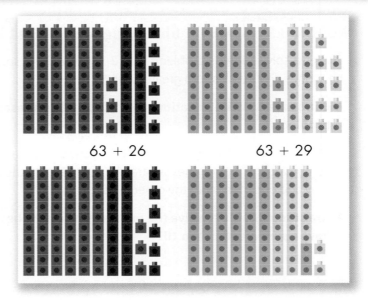

63 + 26   63 + 29

Then direct students' attention to Problems 2 and 3.

What equations represent these two problems? [Write 54 + 32 = _____ and 58 + 36 = _____ on the board.] What strategies did you use to solve them?

Focus the students' attention on the strategy of a student who added by place.

Bridget used adding by place to solve these problems. Let's write the equations that represent what she did.

$$54 + 32 = \underline{\quad} \qquad 58 + 36 = \underline{\quad}$$
$$50 + 30 = 80 \qquad 50 + 30 = 80$$
$$4 + 2 = 6 \qquad 8 + 6 = 14$$
$$80 + 6 = 86 \qquad 80 + 14 = 94$$

Why did Bridget get an answer in the 80s for Problem 2 and an answer in the 90s for Problem 3?

SESSION FOLLOW-UP

4 Daily Practice

 Daily Practice: For reinforcement of this unit's content, have students complete *Student Activity Book* page 14.

 Student Math Handbook: Students and families may use *Student Math Handbook* pages 12–15 for reference and review. See pages 174–181 in the back of this unit.

 Family Letter: Send home copies of the Family Letter (M9–M10).

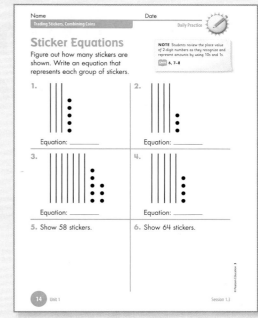

▲ **Student Activity Book, p. 14**

How Many More Stickers to Get 100?

Math Focus Points

◆ Finding the difference between a 2-digit number and 100

Vocabulary

unmarked number line

Today's Plan			Materials
ACTIVITY **① Introducing** *How Many More Stickers to Get 100?*	🕐 15 MIN	👥 CLASS	• T4 🖨 • M12 (2 per student, plus extras)*
ACTIVITY **②** *How Many More Stickers to Get 100?*	🕐 30 MIN	👥 PAIRS	• *Student Activity Book*, pp. 15–16 • M4 (from Session 1.1); M12*
DISCUSSION **③ Representing Strategies on the Number Line**	🕐 15 MIN	👥 CLASS	• *Student Activity Book*, p. 15 • M12
SESSION FOLLOW-UP **④ Daily Practice and Homework**			• *Student Activity Book*, pp. 17–18 • *Student Math Handbook*, pp. 29–30

*See *Materials to Prepare*, p. 23.

Ten-Minute Math

Practicing Place Value: Stickers and Cubes Write the number 52 on the board and ask students to say it to a partner. Make sure all students can read, write, and say this number correctly. Then, ask students to represent the number using cubes.

- How many towers of ten and single cubes did you use?
- How many cubes will you have if you add one more tower of ten to this representation?
- If you add two more towers?
- How about if you subtract two towers of ten?

If time remains, pose similar problems using the number 63.

ACTIVITY

① Introducing *How Many More Stickers to Get 100?*

15 MIN   CLASS

Display the Sticker Book transparency (T4).

At the Sticker Station, you can buy a sticker book to store your stickers in. There are 10 pages in a book. You can put in strips of 10 stickers, single stickers, or a combination of both. This shows what the pages look like without stickers on them. How many stickers can go on one page?

Suppose [Oscar] bought 72 train stickers and put them in his sticker book. What would that look like on this transparency?

Students are likely to suggest filling in 7 rows and 2 squares in the next row. To discourage students from taking the time to color in each square, model simply drawing a line across each row or square to be filled in.

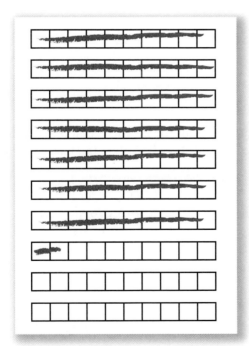

How many more stickers would [Oscar] need to fill a whole page, that is, to have 100 train stickers? Talk with a partner for a couple of minutes, and then we'll share strategies.

Ask two or three students or pairs to share how they solved the problem. As they share, ask questions to reinforce how many 10s and 1s were added on. Help students determine the equations that represent their strategies.

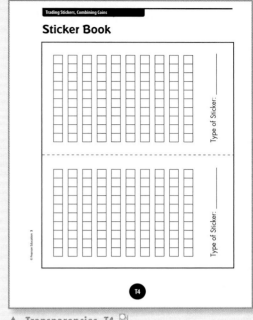

Trading Stickers, Combining Coins

Sticker Book

Type of Sticker: _____

Type of Sticker: _____

T4

▲ **Transparencies, T4**

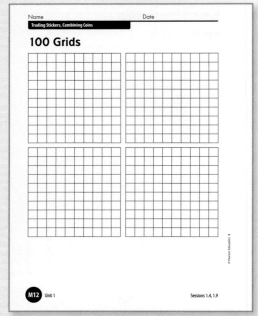

▲ **Resource Masters, M12**

[Bridget and Arthur] started at 72 and counted by 10s to 92. Then they counted by 1s to 100. What equations can we write to show what they did?

Record the equations that students suggest, such as the following:

$$72 + 10 = 82$$
$$82 + 10 = 92$$
$$92 + 1 + 1 + 1 + 1 + 1 + 1 + 1 + 1 = 100$$

Help students think about adding larger chunks and recording more efficiently by directing their attention to the number of 10s and 1s added in their solutions.

How many times did [Bridget and Arthur] count by 10 from 72? How many 1s did they count from 92? How could we write two 10s as a number? What about eight 1s? Let's write the equations again, using these numbers.

As students suggest writing 20 instead of two 10s, and 8 instead of eight 1s, record the new equations.

$$72 + 20 = 92$$
$$92 + 8 = 100$$

How many spaces did they move from 72 to get to 100? Can someone show this on the transparency? Where do you see the 28 spaces in these equations?

As students point out the 20 and 8 that make up the 28 spaces, circle them together and show how they can be added to 72 as a larger chunk.

$$72 + \boxed{20} = 92$$
$$92 + 8 = 100$$

$$20 + 8 = 28, \text{ so } 72 + \underline{28} = 100$$

End this part of the session by handing out copies of 100 Grids (M12).

Each sticker page is ten rows of 10, just like these 100 grids, so you can use these grids to represent sticker book pages. For the rest of math class, you'll work on more problems like the one we just solved. You can use these 100 grids, 100 charts, or the class number line to help you solve them.

ACTIVITY

2 How Many More Stickers to Get 100?

30 MIN   PAIRS

Students work in pairs on *Student Activity Book* pages 15–16. For each problem, they show their strategies by using equations. Remind students that they can use 100 grids or other math tools to help them solve the problems and represent their strategies for solving each one.

A pair of students uses a 100 grid as they solve some sticker problems.

ONGOING ASSESSMENT: Observing Students at Work

Students solve missing addend problems and write equations to represent their work.

- **What strategies do students use?** Do they add or subtract multiples of 10? Do they try to add or subtract amounts that get them to multiples of 10 (e.g., add 8 to 72 first to get to 80, an easy number to work with)?

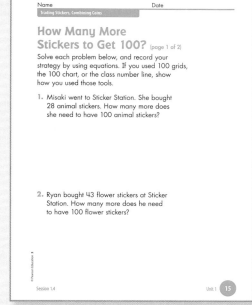

Name _____ Date _____

Trading Stickers, Combining Coins

How Many More Stickers to Get 100? (page 1 of 2)

Solve each problem below, and record your strategy by using equations. If you used 100 grids, the 100 chart, or the class number line, show how you used those tools.

1. Misaki went to Sticker Station. She bought 28 animal stickers. How many more does she need to have 100 animal stickers?

2. Ryan bought 43 flower stickers at Sticker Station. How many more does he need to have 100 flower stickers?

Session 1.4   Unit 1   15

▲ **Student Activity Book, p. 15**   *PORTFOLIO*

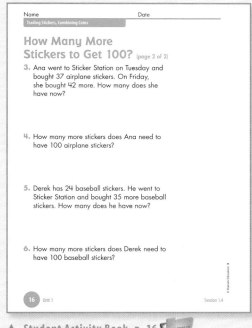

Name _____ Date _____

Trading Stickers, Combining Coins

How Many More Stickers to Get 100? (page 2 of 2)

3. Ana went to Sticker Station on Tuesday and bought 37 airplane stickers. On Friday, she bought 42 more. How many does she have now?

4. How many more stickers does Ana need to have 100 airplane stickers?

5. Derek has 24 baseball stickers. He went to Sticker Station and bought 35 more baseball stickers. How many does he have now?

6. How many more stickers does Derek need to have 100 baseball stickers?

16   Unit 1   Session 1.4

▲ **Student Activity Book, p. 16**   *PORTFOLIO*

- **Are students able to write equations to represent their strategies?**

- **Do students use 100 grids or other tools to help them solve the problems?** Can they represent their solutions on 100 grids or number lines?

DIFFERENTIATION: Supporting the Range of Learners

Intervention The question "How many more?" can be challenging for some students. Acting out the situation with smaller numbers or using a familiar context (You have 72 pennies, but you need 100 pennies; how many more do you need?) can help students visualize the action of the problem. Ask students to identify which number in the problem is the amount of stickers they have, and which number is the number of stickers they are to reach.

DISCUSSION

15 MIN   CLASS

3 Representing Strategies on the Number Line

Math Focus Points for Discussion

◆ Finding the difference between a 2-digit number and 100

Ask a student to read the first problem on *Student Activity Book* page 15: "Misaki went to Sticker Station. She bought 28 animal stickers. How many more does she need to have 100 animal stickers?"

What strategies did you use to solve this problem? Who added to solve the problem? Did anyone use subtraction to solve it?

Most students are likely to have used addition to solve this problem: starting at 28, they add up to 100 and then add the chunks to determine the answer. Some may have used subtraction strategies, starting with 100 and subtracting back by chunks to 28 or subtracting 28 from 100. Highlight both addition and subtraction strategies in this discussion.

Nicholas and Dwayne

"We crossed out 28 spaces on the 100 grid. Then we added 2 more to get to 30. Then we counted by 10 from 30 seven times to get to 100. Seven 10s is 70. 70 + 2 = 72, so she needs 72 more animal stickers."

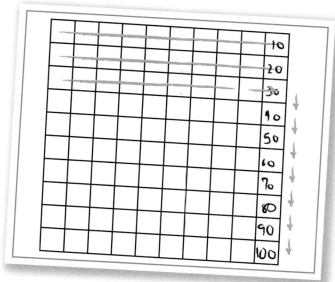

Sample Student Work

Algebra Note

❶ **The Relationship Between Addition and Subtraction** When some students solve a problem by subtracting and others solve the same problem by finding a missing addend, take the opportunity to comment on the relationship between addition and subtraction.

Professional Development

❷ **Teacher Note:** Mathematical Representations for Addition and Subtraction, p. 147

Kelly and Gina

"We didn't use a 100 grid. We added 2 to get to 30. Then we added 20 to get to 50. We know that 50 plus 50 is 100, so we added 50 more to get to 100. We wrote 28 + 2 = 30, 30 + 20 = 50, and 50 + 50 = 100. We added 2 + 20 + 50 together, so she needs 72 more stickers."

Pilar and Adam

"We did something different. She already has 28 stickers. We just subtracted that amount from 100 to figure out how many she still needs. First we did 100 − 20 = 80. Then we did 80 − 8 = 72, so she needs 72 more stickers."

After each pair shares its strategy, record the equations that represent it.❶

Then introduce the unmarked number line.❷

Number lines are useful tools to help solve problems like these or to represent your strategies. You can use a shorthand method of drawing number lines, just like you use a quicker way to draw stickers. [Draw an unmarked number line on the board.] This number line is different because it isn't marked to begin with. You don't need to show all the numbers, just the numbers that are part of the problem you're solving. How many stickers did Misaki start with? How many was she trying to collect?

Math Note

❸ **Representing Subtraction on the Number Line** There are two distinct ways of representing subtraction on the number line. Sometimes students start at 100 and jump back 28, landing on the difference of 72. This method is illustrated on page 59. Other students might think of the number of stickers needed as the distance between 28 and 100 on the number line. In this case, the difference is represented by the jumps from 28 to 100 (or from 100 to 28). Demonstrate whichever methods are used by students in your class.

Mark 28 and 100 on the line, leaving enough room between the two numbers to show the jumps the student made. Refer to the work of students who added up from 28 to 100.

Let's look at Kelly and Gina's strategy on the unmarked number line. They added 2 to 28. Where did they land? I can show that jump like this.

What did they do next?

As students describe the moves, record them on the number line with arched arrows. Label each move and each stopping place.

Record students' methods using equations.

Misaki started with 28 stickers, and she wants to have 100. We can think about the problem this way: 28 + _____ = 100. What number goes in the blank? In other words, how many more stickers does she need? Where do you see this amount on the number line? Where do you see this amount in the equations that represent their strategy?

Help students identify that the sum of the jumps of 2, 20, and 50 on the number line is 72. Therefore, Misaki needs 72 more stickers. Ask students where they see each jump in the equations that represent this strategy.

Now choose another pair of students who subtracted to solve the problem. ❸

Pilar and Adam used subtraction. We can show their strategy on an unmarked number line as well. [Draw a second unmarked number line.] Where did Pilar and Adam start? Let's put 100 on the number line. What did they do first? Then what did they do?

As students describe the steps in this solution, record them on the number line with arched arrows. Label each move and each stopping place.

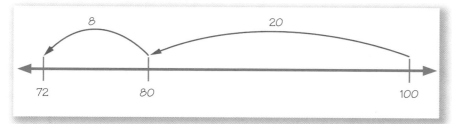

Where do you see the number of stickers that Misaki needs on this number line? What equation represents this strategy?

In this case, the jumps represent the stickers that Misaki already has. By subtracting those from 100—the jumps backward on the number line—we land on 72, the amount of stickers she needs: $100 - 28 = 72$.

SESSION FOLLOW-UP

4 Daily Practice and Homework

 Daily Practice: For reinforcement of this unit's content, have students complete *Student Activity Book* page 17.

 Homework: Students solve problems that involve adding and subtracting 2-digit numbers on *Student Activity Book* page 18.

 Student Math Handbook: Students and families may use *Student Math Handbook* pages 29–30 for reference and review. See pages 174–181 in the back of this unit.

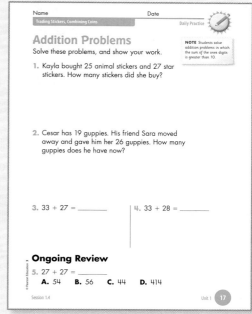

▲ **Student Activity Book, p. 17**

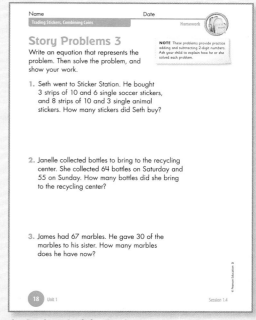

▲ **Student Activity Book, p. 18**

Capture 5: Adding and Subtracting 10s and 1s

Math Focus Points

◆ Adding and subtracting multiples of 10

Today's Plan		Materials
ACTIVITY **① Introducing Capture 5**	20 MIN CLASS	• M13* • T3*; T5* • Overhead colored chips; game piece; pocket 100 chart with colored transparent inserts (optional) • Deck of Change Cards (M14–M15)
ACTIVITY **② Capture 5**	40 MIN PAIRS GROUPS	• Student Activity Book, p. 19 • M4*; M14–M15*; M16 • Overhead colored chips; game pieces
SESSION FOLLOW-UP **③ Daily Practice**		• Student Activity Book, p. 20 • Student Math Handbook, p. G3

*See Materials to Prepare, p. 25.

Ten-Minute Math

Practicing Place Value: Stickers and Cubes Write the number 59 on the board and ask students to say it to a partner. Make sure all students can read, write, and say this number correctly. Then, ask students to represent the number using cubes.

- How many towers of ten and single cubes did you use?
- How many cubes will you have if you add three more tower of ten to this representation?
- If you add four more towers?
- How about if you subtract three towers of ten?

If time remains, pose similar problems using the number 75.

ACTIVITY

① Introducing *Capture 5*

20 MIN | CLASS

Capture 5 is a game that involves students in adding and subtracting 10s and 1s to and from numbers up to 100. Students "capture" chips by moving a game piece on a 100 chart. Moves are determined by Change Cards (M14–M15), labeled in multiples of plus and minus 10s and 1s.❶

Today we're going to learn a game called *Capture 5* that some of you may have played before. In this game you add and subtract combinations of 10s and 1s, and move a game piece around the 100 chart to capture chips. You will have Change Cards that tell you what combinations of moves you can make. You can use one card or up to all five cards to determine your moves.

Set up a demonstration game using a transparency of 100 Chart (T3) and 12 overhead colored chips. (Alternatively, use the pocket 100 chart with the colored transparent inserts.) Place your game piece on the number 54 and one of the chips on the number 46. Place other chips on random squares on the gameboard.

Introduce the game rules. You can make copies of *Capture 5* (M13) as needed.

To demonstrate the way players use Change Cards to determine moves, give yourself the following five Change Cards and display them or draw them on the board.

+20	−10	−3	+2	−30

When it's your turn, you'll look at the five Change Cards you have been dealt. Let's say that these are my five Change Cards. My game piece is on 54, and I want to capture the chip on the number 46. What combination of cards can I use to move from 54 to 46?

As students make suggestions, ask them to explain how they chose their cards. Record suggestions on the board in equation form.❷

$$54 - 10 + 2 = 46$$
$$54 + 2 - 10 = 46$$

Teaching Note

❶ **Capture 5** Some students may have learned *Capture 5* in Grade 2. Students will play the game in its basic form in this unit. Variations are introduced in other units in Grade 3, giving students several opportunities to explore and extend the underlying mathematics of this game.

Math Note

❷ **Order of Operations** The equation $54 - 10 + 2 = 46$ represents the two moves $54 - 10 = 44$ and $44 + 2 = 46$. When expressions include both addition and subtraction, the computation takes place from left to right. Parentheses are used to show a different meaning. For example, $54 - (10 + 2)$ indicates that both 10 and 2 are subtracted from 54. Thus, $54 - (10 + 2) = 54 - 12 = 42$.

Name _____ Date _____
Trading Stickers, Combining Coins

Capture 5

You need
- 100 chart
- Change Cards (deck of 40)
- 12 chips of one color
- game piece for each player
- *Capture 5* Recording Sheet

Play with a partner, or form a team with your partner and play another team of two players.

❶ Place 12 chips on the 100 chart so that each chip is on a different number. Deal five Change Cards to each player or team and place the remaining cards facedown on the table. Players put their game pieces anywhere on the 100 chart to start.

❷ Players or teams take turns trying to capture a chip. On your turn, move your game piece by using any combination of your Change Cards to land on a square with a chip. You can use any number of cards, from one to all five.

❸ If you land exactly on a square with a chip, capture it by taking it off the board. You can capture only one chip during a turn, and it must be from the square you land on.

❹ Record your moves in an equation on the *Capture 5* Recording Sheet. For example, if you begin on 45 and use the cards +2, +10, and +3, you record $45 + 2 + 10 + 3 = 60$.

❺ Place the Change Cards you used facedown in a discard pile. Take cards from the top of the deck to replace them. If the deck of Change Cards is used up, shuffle the discard pile and turn it facedown again.

❻ The first player or team to capture five chips wins.

Sessions 1.5, 1.6, 1.7   Unit 1 M13

▲ **Resource Masters, M13**

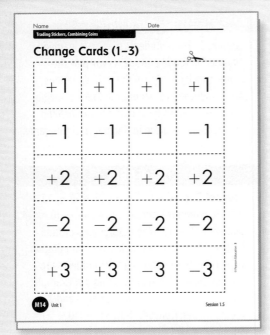

Change Cards (1–3)

+1	+1	+1	+1
−1	−1	−1	−1
+2	+2	+2	+2
−2	−2	−2	−2
+3	+3	−3	−3

M14 Unit 1   Session 1.5

▲ **Resource Masters, M14–M15**

Remove the captured chip and the Change Cards used, and deal yourself 2 new cards. Have students suggest moves to capture another chip and explain how they decided which cards to choose. Use equations to record the moves.

During this demonstration, make sure that students understand the following rules:

- A player can capture only one chip during a turn, and it must be on the last square where the game piece lands.

- Each move must be recorded in equation form on the *Capture 5* Recording Sheet (M16) or *Student Activity Book* page 19. Demonstrate this for students on *Capture 5* Recording Sheet (T5) as you play.

- If students can move, they must do so even if they are not able to capture a chip.

- The first player to capture 5 chips wins the game.

ACTIVITY

2 *Capture 5*

40 MIN   PAIRS   GROUPS

Students play *Capture 5* in pairs or in teams of 4 (with one pair playing the other). Creating teams encourages conversation between team members about possible moves. Remind students to record their equations on their recording sheets as they play.

As students play Capture 5, *they add and subtract multiples of 10.*

ONGOING ASSESSMENT: Observing Students at Work

Students practice adding and subtracting multiples of 10 and single-digit numbers by playing the game *Capture 5*.

- **Do students make jumps of 10, rather than counting out 10 by 1s?** Can they make multiple jumps of 10?

- **Do students try to capture chips by trial and error?** Or do they determine the distance from their game piece to a chip, and look for combinations of Change Cards that will make up that distance?

- **Can students write equations that accurately reflect their moves from one number to another?**

- **Are students demonstrating knowledge of the effect of combining forward and backward moves (e.g., using +30 and −10 cards to move forward 20 spaces)?**

DIFFERENTIATION: Supporting the Range of Learners

Intervention If some students are moving their game pieces by counting by 1s, help them make moves in larger chunks. Point out that they might model their moves with stickers or cubes to remind them of the work they have done with adding and subtracting 10s.

- I see your game piece is on 27 and you have the Change Card +10. What does 27 look like with stickers or cubes?

- What number would you have if you added one more strip of 10? Can you see that number on the 100 chart? Where would you move on the 100 chart if you added another 10?

1	2	3	4	5	6	7	8	9	10
11	12	13	14	15	16	17	18	19	20
21	22	23	24	25	26	27	~~28~~	~~29~~	~~30~~
~~31~~	~~32~~	~~33~~	~~34~~	~~35~~	~~36~~	37	38	39	40
41	42	43	44	45	46	47	48	49	50

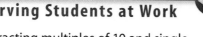

Name _____ Date _____

Trading Stickers, Combining Coins

Capture 5 Recording Sheet

Record your starting number, the changes you use, and your ending number for each move, like this:

16 + 10 + 10 − 2 = 34

Session 1.5   Unit 1   19

▲ Student Activity Book, p. 19; Resource Masters, M16; T5

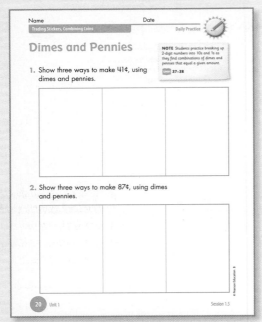

▲ **Student Activity Book, p. 20**

For those students who are moving around the board by trial and error, help them consider number relationships to determine the best moves.

Your game piece is on 43, and you want to capture the chip on 21. How far apart are those numbers? . . . Yes, they are 22 spaces apart. Is there a combination of cards you can use that will let you move back 22 spaces?

SESSION FOLLOW-UP
③ Daily Practice

 Daily Practice: For reinforcement of this unit's content, have students complete *Student Activity Book* page 20.

 Student Math Handbook: Students and families may use *Student Math Handbook* page G3 for reference and review. See pages 174–181 in the back of this unit.

Assessment: Adding and Subtracting 10s

Math Focus Points

◆ Using equivalencies among pennies, dimes, and dollars

◆ Adding pennies and dimes to sums up to $2.00

◆ Adding and subtracting multiples of 10

Vocabulary

penny
dime
dollar

Today's Plan		Materials
① **ACTIVITY** **Introducing** *Collect $2.00*	15 MIN · CLASS	• M17; T6; T7 • Pennies, Dimes, and Dollars Set*; number cubes 1–6 and 7–12
② **MATH WORKSHOP** **Assessment: Adding and Subtracting 10s** **2A** *Collect $2.00* **2B** *Capture 5* **2C** *How Many More to 100? How Much More to $1.00?*	45 MIN	• M3 ☑ **2A** • *Student Activity Book*, p. 21 • M18; M19 • Pennies, Dimes, and Dollars Sets; number cubes 1–6 and 7–12 **2B** • Materials from Session 1.5, p. 60. Use M19 in place of *Student Activity Book*, p. 19. **2C** • *Student Activity Book*, pp. 22–23
③ **SESSION FOLLOW-UP** **Daily Practice and Homework**	PAIRS	• *Student Activity Book*, pp. 24–25 • *Student Math Handbook*, pp. 36, 37–38; G6

*See *Materials to Prepare*, p. 25.

Ten-Minute Math

Practicing Place Value Write the following problems on the board and ask students to solve them (mentally, if possible).

$$48 + 20 \quad 48 - 10 \quad 48 + 40$$

Write each answer on the board and ask students to compare each sum or difference with 48.

• Which places have the same digits? Which do not? Why?

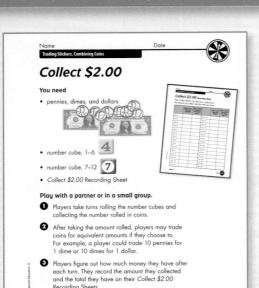

▲ Resource Masters, M17

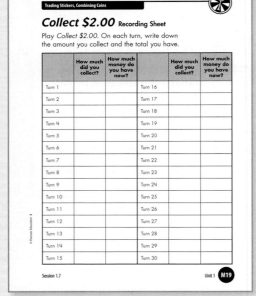

▲ Resource Masters, M19; T7

15 MIN   CLASS

ACTIVITY

Introducing *Collect $2.00*

Because the related games *Collect 25¢, Collect 50¢,* and *Collect $1.00* were introduced in Grade 2, many students will be familiar with the basic structure of *Collect $2.00.* Many will also know the equivalence of 1 dollar to 10 dimes and of 1 dime to 10 pennies. In this version of *Collect $2.00,* students play with pennies, dimes, and dollars as another representation of 1s, 10s, and 100s. The goal is to collect $2.00.

Play a couple of demonstration rounds with students to introduce the game. For this demonstration, you and the students will play as a team. You will need one Pennies, Dimes, and Dollars Set; number cubes 1–6 and 7–12; and transparencies of 200 Chart (T6) and *Collect $2.00* Recording Sheet (T7). Also have available copies of the *Collect $2.00* game rules (M17).

Begin by rolling the two number cubes and discussing which coins you can take.

I rolled a 5 and a 9. How much is that? What combination of pennies and dimes can we take to make 14¢?

Record the result of that round on the transparency of the *Collect $2.00* Recording Sheet (T7).

Explain that for each turn, a player rolls the two number cubes again. Do this, and then discuss what coins you can take. Add them to the coins from the first roll. Then discuss possible trades you can make.

On our first turn, we rolled 14 and took 1 dime and 4 pennies. Then we rolled 8, and we took 8 pennies. How many pennies do we have now? Are there any trades we can make?

Agree together on any trades, and make them. In this case, 10 pennies can be traded for one dime, leaving 2 pennies. Then work together to figure out how much money there is altogether, and record it on the recording sheet transparency.

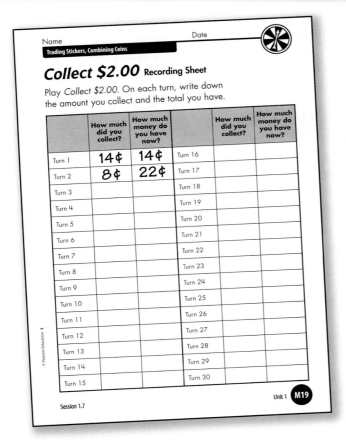

▲ Resource Masters, M18; T6

We traded 10 pennies for a dime. Now we have 2 dimes and 2 pennies. How much money do we have? How do you know? How much more do we need to get to 30¢? To 50¢? How about to get to a dollar? ❶

As you discuss students' strategies for figuring this out, highlight the connection between 100 cents and $1.00.

When I asked how much more we needed to get to one dollar, why did you figure out how far it was from 22 to 100? What does 100 have to do with $1.00?

Display the transparency 200 Chart (T6), and let students know that they can use this chart as a tool while playing *Collect $2.00.*

How much more do we need to get to $2.00? Can you show how you figured this out on the 200 chart?

Take a few more turns as a team, discussing the trades you can make and how far you are from $1.00 and $2.00. Record each round. Explain that at the end of the game, students do not have to make a trade that equals exactly $2.00; any amount that takes them over $2.00 is sufficient.

Math Note

❶ **Counting with Coins** When students play this game, some take the coins and then consider possible trades. Others mentally combine the new roll with the previous total and make trades immediately, as they are taking the new coins. Use the former method for the whole-class introduction because it gives students an opportunity to revisit the equivalence of 10 pennies to 1 dime, 10 dimes to 1 dollar, and 100 pennies to 1 dollar. It also allows them to see the trades more clearly.

Teaching Note

❷ Math Workshop Although many students will be familiar with the structure of Math Workshop from previous grades, it is important to spend time in this session laying the foundations for what it means to have a productive Math Workshop time. Students may need to be reminded to work cooperatively with a partner and to stay focused on the mathematics of each activity. For ideas about how to communicate expectations for this and other beginning-of-the-year Math Workshops, see *Implementing Investigations in Grade 3*.

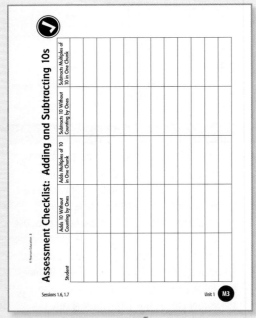

▲ Resource Masters, M3 ✓

 Assessment: Adding and Subtracting 10s

 45 MIN

In this Math Workshop, students have their choice of three activities.❷ They can play *Collect $2.00*, play *Capture 5*, or solve problems in which they find the difference between 2-digit numbers and 100. As you observe students, in this and the next session, working on these three activities, you will be assessing their ability to add and subtract 10 and multiples of 10. Use the Assessment Checklist: Adding and Subtracting 10s (M3) to record your observations for each student. This assessment addresses Benchmark 2.

2A *Collect $2.00*

PAIRS

Players take turns rolling the set of number cubes and collecting that amount in pennies and dimes. After each turn, players can trade for equivalent coins. Then they record their turn, figuring out how much money they have so far. The goal is to collect $2.00. Make available copies of 200 Chart (M18) for students to use if they wish.

Students take turns rolling the number cubes, but work cooperatively to collect $2.00.

ONGOING ASSESSMENT: Observing Students at Work

Students use the equivalence of 10 pennies and 1 dime and of 10 dimes and 1 dollar to make trades and practice adding amounts up to $2.00 (200 pennies).

- **Do students know coin names, values, and basic equivalencies?**

- **How do students decide what coins to take?** How do they decide what trades to make? How fluent are they with the equivalence of 10 pennies to 1 dime and 10 dimes to 1 dollar?

- **How do students total their coins?** Can they count by 10s and add on the pennies?

- **How do students figure out how much they need to make a multiple of 10?** $1.00? $2.00?

As you observe, ask students to count the money they have so far, and to figure out how much more they need to reach a multiple of 10, $1.00, or $2.00.

DIFFERENTIATION: Supporting the Range of Learners

Intervention If some students are struggling with coin equivalencies, work with them in a small group. Consider starting with a simpler version of the game, *Collect 50¢* or *Collect $1.00*. (See the Grade 2 unit, *Counting, Coins, and Combinations*.)

ELL In order to participate in this activity, English Language Learners must know the names and values of U.S. coins. To reinforce this knowledge, make three sets of cards: one set with pictures of the coins taped to the cards, one set with the names of the coins, and one set with their values. Then students can play a variation of *Go Fish,* asking their partner for the cards they need to make a complete set (e.g., a picture of a penny, the word "penny," and the term "one cent").

2B *Capture 5*

PAIRS

For complete details about this activity, see Session 1.5.

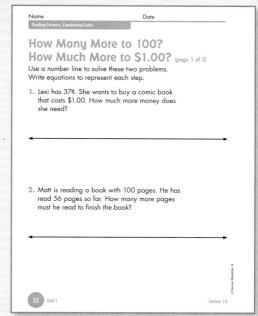

▲ **Student Activity Book, p. 22**

▲ **Student Activity Book, p. 23**

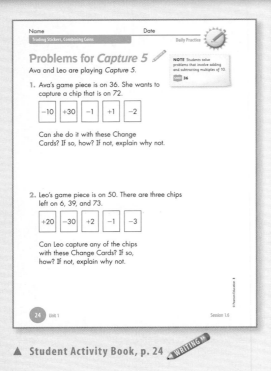

Name **Trading Stickers, Combining Coins** Date

Daily Practice

Problems for *Capture 5*

Ava and Leo are playing *Capture 5*.

NOTE Students solve problems that involve adding and subtracting multiples of 10.
Skill 36

1. Ava's game piece is on 36. She wants to capture a chip that is on 72.

| −10 | +30 | −1 | +1 | −2 |

Can she do it with these Change Cards? If so, how? If not, explain why not.

2. Leo's game piece is on 50. There are three chips left on 6, 39, and 73.

| +20 | −30 | +2 | −1 | −3 |

Can Leo capture any of the chips with these Change Cards? If so, how? If not, explain why not.

24   Unit 1   Session 1.6

▲ Student Activity Book, p. 24

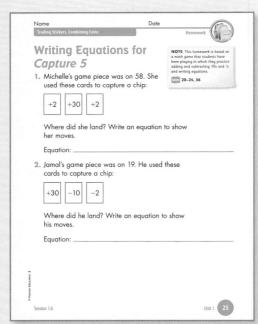

Name **Trading Stickers, Combining Coins** Date

Homework

Writing Equations for *Capture 5*

NOTE This homework is based on a math game that students have been playing in which they practice adding and subtracting 10s and 1s and writing equations.
Skill 20–24, 36

1. Michelle's game piece was on 58. She used these cards to capture a chip:

| +2 | +30 | +2 |

Where did she land? Write an equation to show her moves.

Equation: _____

2. Jamal's game piece was on 19. He used these cards to capture a chip:

| +30 | −10 | −2 |

Where did he land? Write an equation to show his moves.

Equation: _____

Session 1.6   Unit 1   25

▲ Student Activity Book, p. 25

2C How Many More to 100? How Much More to $1.00?

PAIRS

Students solve the problems on *Student Activity Book* pages 22–23 and write the equations that represent their work. Make sure that students understand that they are to use the unmarked number lines to solve these problems or represent their strategies.

ONGOING ASSESSMENT: Observing Students at Work

Students solve problems in which they determine the difference between 2-digit numbers and 100 or $1.00.

- **Are students able to write equations to represent their steps?**

- **Are they able to use number lines to solve the problems or to represent their strategies?**

- **How large are the jumps that students make on the number line?** Do they add or subtract multiples of 10? Do they add or subtract to get numbers that are easy to work with, such as multiples of 10 (e.g., adding 3 to 37 to get 40)?

DIFFERENTIATION: Supporting the Range of Learners

Intervention If some students are having difficulty using number lines to solve these problems or represent their solutions, work with them in small groups. Solve the first problem together by using the class number line, identifying the starting and ending numbers and each stopping place along the way. Then help the students represent each move on the unmarked number line that accompanies Problem 1.

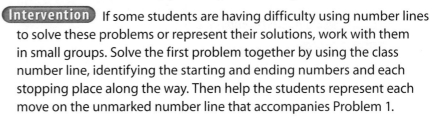

SESSION FOLLOW-UP

3 Daily Practice and Homework

Daily Practice: For reinforcement of this unit's content, have students complete *Student Activity Book* page 24.

Homework: Students solve problems on *Student Activity Book* page 25, based on the game *Capture 5*.

Student Math Handbook: Students and families may use *Student Math Handbook* pages 36, 37–38 and G6 for reference and review. See pages 174–181 in the back of this unit.

Strategies for Capture 5

Math Focus Points

◆ Adding and subtracting multiples of 10

◆ Adding pennies and dimes to sums up to $2.00

◆ Finding the difference between a 2-digit number and 100

Today's Plan		Materials
DISCUSSION **①** **Strategies for** *Capture 5*	20 MIN · CLASS	• T3 • Game pieces; overhead colored chips
MATH WORKSHOP **②** **Addition and Subtraction with Tens and Ones** **2A** *Capture 5* **2B** *Collect $2.00* **2C** *How Many More to 100? How Much More to $1.00?* **2D** *How Many More? How Much More?*	40 MIN	**2A** • Materials from Session 1.5, p. 60 Use M16 in place of *Student Activity Book,* p. 19. **2B** • Materials from Session 1.6, p. 65 Use M19 in place of *Student Activity Book,* p. 21. **2C** • *Student Activity Book,* pp. 22–23 **2D** • *Student Activity Book,* pp. 27–29
SESSION FOLLOW-UP **③** **Daily Practice**		• *Student Activity Book,* p. 30 • *Student Math Handbook,* pp. 36, 37–38; G3, G6

*See *Materials to Prepare,* p. 25.

Ten-Minute Math

Practicing Place Value Write the following problems on the board and ask students to solve them (mentally, if possible).

$67 + 10$ $67 - 30$ $67 + 50$

Write each answer on the board and ask students to compare each sum or difference with 67.

Which places have the same digits? Which do not? Why?

Professional Development

❶ **Dialogue Box:** Strategies for *Capture 5*, p. 171

DISCUSSION

Strategies for *Capture 5*

20 MIN   CLASS

Math Focus Points for Discussion

◆ Adding and subtracting multiples of 10

After playing *Capture 5*, some students have very clear plans or strategies for moving on the 100 chart. First, they may consider the distance between their game piece and the number under the chip they are trying to capture. Next, they may use their knowledge of adding and subtracting multiples of 10 and combine addition and subtraction to determine their moves. Other students may still use a trial-and-error approach, making random moves in an effort to capture a chip. This discussion can give you a sense of how students are approaching the game.❶

Display the transparency 100 Chart (T3) with a game piece on 34 and a chip on 56. Draw the following Change Cards on the board.

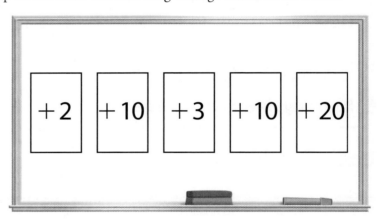

Suppose that you are playing *Capture 5*. Your game piece is on 34, and you want to capture a chip on 56. What combination of these Change Cards could you use to move from 34 to 56?

As students respond, record their suggestions in the form of equations.

Students might say:

"I can use a plus 10 card to get to 44, another plus 10 card to get to 54, and a plus 2 card to get to 56."

$$34 + 10 + 10 + 2 = 56$$

"34 plus 20 gets me to 54, plus 2 more gets me to the marker on 56."

$$34 + 20 + 2 = 56$$

Erase the first set of Change Cards, and draw these five:

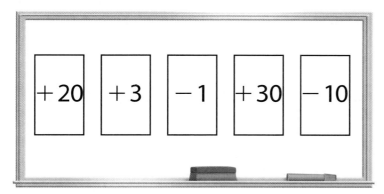

Suppose that the game starts the same way, with your game piece on 34. Can you use a combination of plus and minus cards to capture that chip on 56? Work alone or with a partner to come up with this kind of combination.

After a few minutes, call students back together and ask for volunteers to share their card combinations.

Expect a range of responses. Some students will add or subtract 10 or multiples of 10 first and then determine what combinations of 1s will get them to the desired chip. Others may add or subtract 1s first in an effort to match the ones digits in the starting and ending numbers.

Students might say:

"We added 20 to get to 54. Then we used a plus 3 card to get to 57 and a minus 1 card to move to 56."

$$34 + 20 + 3 - 1 = 56$$

"I wanted to make 36 first so that I could move by tens. I added 3 to make 37. Then I had to subtract 1 to get to 36. Then I jumped 30 to 66 and had to subtract 10 to get to 56."

$$34 + 3 - 1 + 30 - 10 = 56$$

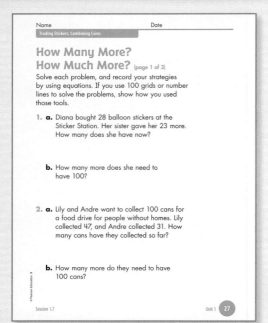

▲ Student Activity Book, p. 27

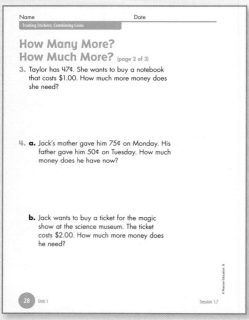

▲ Student Activity Book, p. 28

As students share strategies, check for understanding by asking other students to explain the moves. For example:

How did Benjamin know that a +20 card would get him to 54? Ines moved to 36 and then used a +30 card and a −10 card to get to 56. How many spaces did she have to move? How did a +30 and −10 card move her that many spaces?

To help students understand the effect of combining forward and backward moves (moving 30 spaces forward and 10 spaces back results in a forward move of 20 spaces), ask students who also made these moves to demonstrate them on the 100 chart at the overhead.

MATH WORKSHOP

2 Addition and Subtraction with Tens and Ones

40 MIN

In this Math Workshop, students continue to play *Capture 5* and *Collect $2.00*, and solve problems in which they find the difference between a number and 100 or 200. Continue to use the Assessment Checklist: Adding and Subtracting 10s (M3) to record observations about students' ability to add and subtract tens. Keep Math Workshop materials available after this session because students may return to these activities if they have time after finishing the assessment in Session 1.9.

2A *Capture 5*

PAIRS

For complete details about this activity, see Session 1.5, pages 61–62.

2B *Collect $2.00*

PAIRS

For complete details about this activity, see Session 1.6, pages 66–67.

2C *How Many More to 100? How Much More to $1.00?*

PAIRS

For complete details about this activity, see Session 1.6, page 70.

2D *How Many More? How Much More?*

INDIVIDUALS

Students solve problems on *Student Activity Book* pages 27–29, in which they determine the difference between a number and 100 or 200.

ONGOING ASSESSMENT: Observing Students at Work

Students solve story problems in which they add 2-digit numbers and find the difference between those calculated sums and 100 or 200.

- **Do students correctly interpret what is happening in each problem?**

- **Do students have addition strategies they can carry out fluently and accurately?** Do they add by place or add on one number in parts?

- **How do students solve the missing addend problems?** Do they use multiples of 10 to solve them? What representations do students use to help them solve the problems?

SESSION FOLLOW-UP

③ Daily Practice

 Daily Practice: For reinforcement of this unit's content, have students complete *Student Activity Book* page 30.

 Student Math Handbook: Students and families may use *Student Math Handbook* pages 36, 37–38 and G3, G6 for reference and review. See pages 174–181 in the back of this unit.

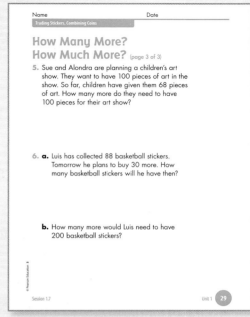

Name _____ Date _____
Trading Stickers, Combining Coins

How Many More?
How Much More? (page 3 of 3)

5. Sue and Alondra are planning a children's art show. They want to have 100 pieces of art in the show. So far, children have given them 68 pieces of art. How many more do they need to have 100 pieces for their art show?

6. **a.** Luis has collected 88 basketball stickers. Tomorrow he plans to buy 30 more. How many basketball stickers will he have then?

b. How many more would Luis need to have 200 basketball stickers?

Session 1.7   Unit 1   29

▲ **Student Activity Book, p. 29**

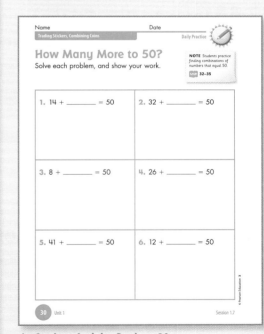

Name _____ Date _____
Trading Stickers, Combining Coins   Daily Practice

How Many More to 50?
Solve each problem, and show your work.

NOTE Students practice finding combinations of numbers that equal 50
32–35

1. $14 + \underline{\quad} = 50$	2. $32 + \underline{\quad} = 50$
3. $8 + \underline{\quad} = 50$	4. $26 + \underline{\quad} = 50$
5. $41 + \underline{\quad} = 50$	6. $12 + \underline{\quad} = 50$

30   Unit 1   Session 1.7

▲ **Student Activity Book, p. 30**

Making Numbers with 100s, 10s, and 1s

Math Focus Points

◆ Recognizing and representing the place value of each digit in 2- and 3-digit numbers

◆ Finding different combinations of 100s, 10s, and 1s for a number, and recognizing their equivalence (i.e., 1 hundred, 3 tens, and 7 ones equals 1 hundred, 2 tens, and 17 ones, or 13 tens and 7 ones)

◆ Recognizing and demonstrating the equivalence of one 100 to ten 10s and of one 10 to ten 1s

Today's Plan		Materials
① ACTIVITY **Introducing Sticker Combinations: 37 Stickers**	10 MIN · CLASS · INDIVIDUALS	• Cubes, in towers of 10
② ACTIVITY **Sticker Combinations: 137 Stickers**	30 MIN · CLASS · PAIRS	• *Student Activity Book,* pp. 31–32 • T8*
③ DISCUSSION **137 Stickers**	20 MIN · CLASS · PAIRS	• Chart: "Ways to Make 137"*
④ SESSION FOLLOW-UP **Daily Practice and Homework**		• *Student Activity Book,* pp. 33–34 • *Student Math Handbook,* pp. 7–8, 9

*See *Materials to Prepare,* p. 25.

Ten-Minute Math

Practicing Place Value Show 49 stickers on the overhead using transparent strips of 10 and singles. Have students use cubes to represent the number.

What number does the image represent? How do you know?

Add 2 more strips of 10 to (or remove 2 strips of 10 from) the overhead and have students represent the new number with cubes.

What number does the image represent now? What is the relationship between this new number and the first number?

If time remains, pose similar problems using the number 27.

ACTIVITY

Introducing Sticker Combinations: 37 Stickers

10 MIN   CLASS   INDIVIDUALS

Suppose that you went to Sticker Station and bought 37 stickers. What different combinations of strips and singles could you buy to make 37? Take a couple of minutes to work on this problem. Use cubes or sketch the stickers to show the combinations that you find.❶

Students should have no problem representing 37 as three strips of 10 and 7 singles. However, they may not immediately see that 37 can also be represented as 2 strips of 10 and 17 singles, one strip of 10 and 27 singles, or 37 singles. If students appear to be having trouble with this, ask questions such as the following:

I see that Jane used three strips of 10 and seven singles to represent the first equation. What if you could buy only two strips of 10? How many singles would you also have to buy to make 37 stickers in all? What if you could buy only one strip of 10? Can you make 37 with only singles?

As students share their combinations of stickers, start a chart on the board. Sketch each combination, and then record it as strips, singles, tens, and ones. Ask students what equation represents each combination and record this as well. Record the equations with the 37 followed by the equal sign: $37 = 30 + 7$.❷

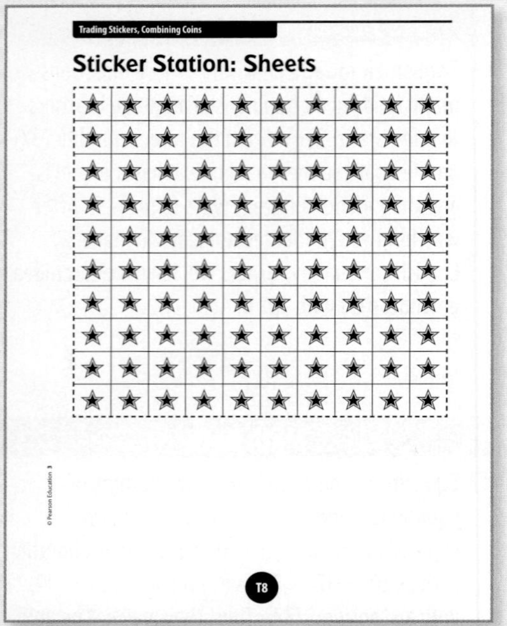

Trading Stickers, Combining Coins

Sticker Station: Sheets

© Pearson Education 3

T8

▲ **Transparencies, T8**

Picture	Strips and Singles	Tens and Ones	Equation
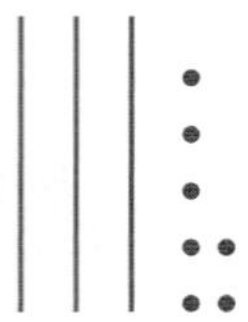	3 strips + 7 singles	3 tens + 7 ones	$37 = 30 + 7$
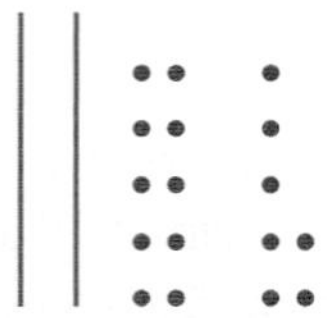	2 strips + 17 singles	2 tens + 17 ones	$37 = 20 + 17$
	1 strip + 27 singles	1 ten + 27 ones	$37 = 10 + 27$
	0 strips + 37 singles	0 tens + 37 ones	$37 = 0 + 37$

As students look at the chart, they may notice that the number of singles increases by 10, each time one less strip of 10 is used. This pattern will be explored further in the activity and the discussion that follow.

ACTIVITY

2 Sticker Combinations: 137 Stickers

30 MIN   CLASS   PAIRS

Display the transparency of Sticker Station: Sheets (T8).

People sometimes like to buy stickers in large amounts. Because of this, the people who run Sticker Station decided to sell large sheets of stickers as well as strips of 10 and singles. How many stickers are there in a sheet? How do you know? Take a minute to talk to the person next to you about this question.

Students might say:

"The sheet contains ten rows of 10, just like a page in a sticker book. Ten groups of 10 is equal to 100."

Ask a volunteer to point to the 10 groups of 10 on the transparency. Count aloud by 10s to 100.

You figured out that there are 100 stickers in a sheet. We already have a quick way to draw strips of 10 and singles by using lines and dots. To sketch a sheet of 100, we can draw a square. We'll know that that means 100 without having to show every sticker.

Demonstrate what you mean by drawing a square, 4 lines, and 5 dots on the board, and asking students how many stickers that represents.

Now imagine that you want to buy 137 stickers. Work with a partner to find as many different ways as you can to make 137 stickers.

Some students interpret this problem to mean that each combination needs to involve sheets, strips, *and* singles. Thus, they think that 13 strips and 7 singles or 137 singles are not valid answers. Take a moment to clarify that combinations do not have to include all three ways in which stickers are sold.❸ For example:

What if you went to Sticker Station and they were all out of sheets of 100? How can you make 137 by using only strips of 10 and singles? What if they only had ten strips of 10 left? Then what could you buy to get 137?

Explain that students will record all the different ways they find on *Student Activity Book* pages 31–32. Remind students that they can use cubes or sketch stickers to help them.

Math Note

❸ **Possible Combinations** There are 18 possible combinations of sheets, strips, and singles for 137 stickers. Although some students may find all the possible combinations, do not expect all students to do so.

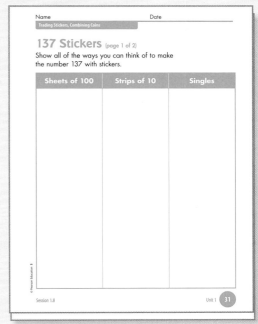

▲ **Student Activity Book, pp. 31–32**

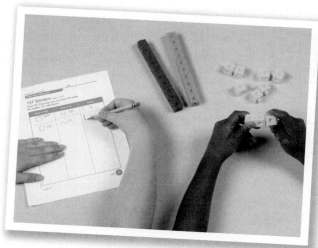

Sketching stickers and using cubes help students find different combinations of 100s, 10s, and 1s that equal 137.

ONGOING ASSESSMENT: Observing Students at Work

Students find ways to represent 137 with 100s, 10s, and 1s.

- **Do students' solutions demonstrate knowledge that ten strips of 10 are equivalent to one sheet of 100?** That one sheet of 100 and three strips of 10 are equal to 13 strips of 10?

- **Are students able to generate multiple combinations of sheets, strips, and singles that total 137?** Do they see connections between the different solutions? Do they find most or all of them?

- **How do students record their work?** Do they use pictures? Numbers? Both?

DIFFERENTIATION: Supporting the Range of Learners

Intervention Some students may need additional work representing all the possible combinations for 2-digit numbers before moving on to finding the combinations for 137. Choose a 2-digit number between 50 and 99 for these students to represent. If students are successful with this, have them find combinations of sheets, strips, and singles for 100 stickers.

Extension Students who move easily through this activity should be encouraged to find all possible combinations of stickers for 137. Ask them to think about how they could organize their combinations to prove that they have them all.

20 MIN   CLASS   PAIRS

DISCUSSION

③ 137 Stickers

Math Focus Points for Discussion

◆ Finding different combinations of 100s, 10s, and 1s for a number, and recognizing their equivalence (i.e., 1 hundred, 3 tens, and 7 ones equals 1 hundred, 2 tens, and 17 ones, or 13 tens and 7 ones)

◆ Recognizing and demonstrating the equivalence of one 100 to ten 10s and of one 10 to ten 1s

Call students together to discuss their work on finding combinations that make 137 stickers. On the board, list students' combinations as they are shared, writing them as sheets, strips, and singles. During the discussion, you will select examples from this list to add to the Ways to Make 137 chart you prepared ahead of time.

Because all students are likely to have come up with the combination of 1 sheet, 3 strips, and 7 singles, start by writing this combination on the chart. Model (or have a student model) this combination with cubes or stickers, and draw a sketch of this combination in the first column of the chart. Ask students to help you write this combination as hundreds, tens, and ones, and as an equation.

Ways to Make 137			
Picture	Sheets, Strips, and Singles	Hundreds, Tens, and Ones	Equation
	1 sheet 3 strips 7 singles	1 hundred 3 tens 7 ones	$100 + 30 + 7 = 137$

Choose another combination that includes one sheet of 100, and record it under the first combination, such as 1 sheet, 2 strips, 17 singles.

Here's another combination of stickers that you found to equal 137. The first combination has 3 strips of 10, but the second combination has only 2. What happened to the third strip of 10?

Give students a few minutes to explore this question with a partner, sketching the stickers if needed. Then ask partners to share their ideas with the class. Listen for understanding that in the second combination, one strip of 10 is now represented by 10 ones. Ask a student to demonstrate this with cubes.

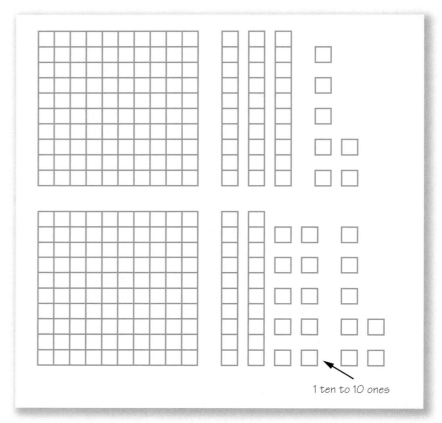

1 ten to 10 ones

How can we write this combination (1 sheet, 2 strips, and 17 singles) as hundreds, tens, and ones? *(1 hundred + 2 tens + 17 ones)* As an equation? *(100 + 20 + 17 = 137)*

Record these on the chart as well.

To help students understand the equivalence of one sheet of 100 to ten strips of 10, choose a combination without sheets. Follow the same procedure as above, asking students to name the combination as hundreds, tens, and ones, and as an equation.

Then choose a second combination that includes no sheets, and add it to the chart in the same way.

Picture	Sheets, Strips, and Singles	Hundreds, Tens, and Ones	Equation
	1 sheet 3 strips 7 singles	1 hundred 3 tens 7 ones	100 + 30 + 7 = 137
	1 sheet 2 strips 17 singles	1 hundred 2 tens 17 ones	100 + 20 + 17 = 137
	0 sheet 13 strips 7 singles	0 hundreds 13 tens 7 ones	0 + 130 + 7 = 137
	0 sheet 11 strips 27 singles	0 hundreds 11 tens 27 ones	0 + 110 + 27 = 137

The last two combinations we've put on our chart include no sheets of 100. If the number of stickers is 137, how can we have a combination that doesn't have a sheet of 100? Where is the 100 in this group of stickers? Why is the number of singles different in these two sticker pictures? Work with a partner to answer these questions.

After a few minutes, ask pairs to share their answers. To help make the equivalence of 100 and ten 10s clear to all students, invite a pair to demonstrate these relationships on the overhead, using cubes or transparent stickers.

▲ Student Activity Book, p. 33

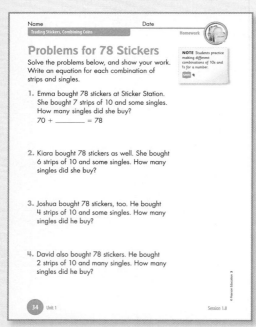

▲ Student Activity Book, p. 34

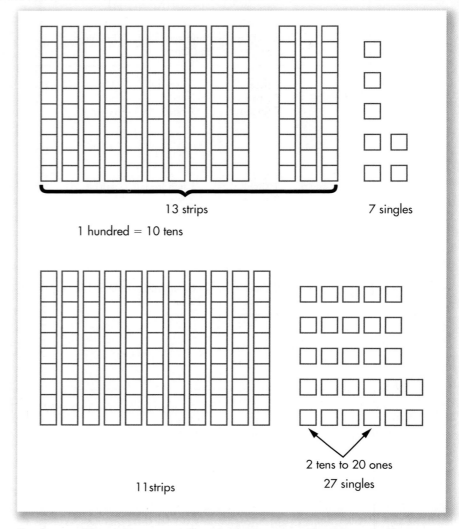

Students will continue to work with these types of problems in the next session and in Investigation 2.

SESSION FOLLOW-UP
4 Daily Practice and Homework

Daily Practice: For reinforcement of this unit's content, have students complete *Student Activity Book* page 33.

Homework: Students solve problems about combinations of 10s and 1s on *Student Activity Book* page 34.

Student Math Handbook: Students and families may use *Student Math Handbook* pages 7–8, 9 for reference and review. See pages 174–181 in the back of this unit.

Assessment: Hundreds, Tens, and Ones

Math Focus Points

◈ Recognizing and demonstrating the equivalence of one 100 to ten 10s and of one 10 to ten 1s

◈ Solving addition problems with 2-digit numbers by using strategies that involve breaking numbers apart by place or adding one number in parts

◈ Finding the difference between a 2-digit number and 100

◈ Finding different combinations of 100s, 10s, and 1s for a number and recognizing their equivalence (i.e., 1 hundred, 3 tens, and 7 ones equals 1 hundred, 2 tens, and 17 ones, or 13 tens and 7 ones)

Today's Plan		Materials
DISCUSSION **1 Trading 100s, 10s, and 1s**	20 MIN CLASS PAIRS	• M12*; M18* • Cubes, in towers of 10; pennies, dimes, and dollars sets; chart paper or board: problem for discussion*
ASSESSMENT ACTIVITY **2 Hundreds, Tens, and Ones**	✓ 40 MIN INDIVIDUALS	• M21–M22*
SESSION FOLLOW-UP **3 Daily Practice**		• *Student Activity Book,* p. 35 • *Student Math Handbook,* pp. 7–8, 37–38

*See *Materials to Prepare,* p. 25.

Ten-Minute Math

Practicing Place Value Show 84 stickers on the overhead using transparent strips of 10 and singles. Have students use cubes to represent the number.

What number does the image represent?

How do you know?

Add 1 more strip of 10 to (or remove 5 strips of 10 from) the overhead and have students represent the new number with cubes.

What number does the image represent now?

How many towers of 10 and single cubes did you use to represent it?

If time remains, pose similar problems using the number 91.

DISCUSSION
Trading 100s, 10s, and 1s

20 MIN   CLASS   PAIRS

Math Focus Points for Discussion

◆ Recognizing and demonstrating the equivalence of one 100 and ten 10s and of one 10 and ten 1s

Display the following problem on chart paper or on the board, and ask a volunteer to read it aloud:

> Max is playing *Collect $2.00*, but he keeps forgetting to trade his coins. He has 13 dimes and 23 pennies. How much money does he have?

Take a few minutes to work with a partner to figure out how much money Max has now. Use cubes or your pennies, dimes, and dollars to show that your answer is correct.

Give students about five minutes to work on the problem. Then call them together to share their strategies and representations. Students should be able to demonstrate with coins or cubes the equivalence of 10 dimes to 1 dollar and 10 pennies to 1 dime. Record students' responses, writing the equivalencies on the board.

Students might say:

"Max has 13 dimes. I know that 10 dimes equal 1 dollar, so I can trade in 10 of his dimes for a dollar. That leaves him with 3 dimes."

10 dimes = 1 dollar
    so
13 dimes = 1 dollar + 3 dimes

"He also has 23 pennies. I know that 10 pennies equal 1 dime, so I can trade in 23 pennies for 2 dimes with 3 pennies left over."

10 pennies = 1 dime
      so
20 pennies = 2 dimes
      and
23 pennies = 2 dimes + 3 pennies

You've shown that Max can trade his 13 dimes for 1 dollar and 3 dimes and his 23 pennies for 2 dimes and 3 pennies. What will Max have after he makes these trades? How much money is that? How much more money does Max need to get to $2.00? Work with your partner to figure that out. You can use a 200 chart or unmarked number line to help you.

As students share strategies, invite volunteers to show how they can find the difference between $1.53 and $2.00, using an unmarked number line or the 200 chart.

Students might say:

"We added 7¢ to $1.53 to get to $1.60 and then we jumped by 10s four times to $2.00. That's 47 in all, so he needs 47¢ more."

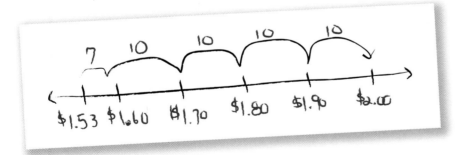

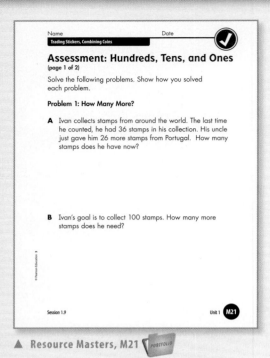

▲ Resource Masters, M21

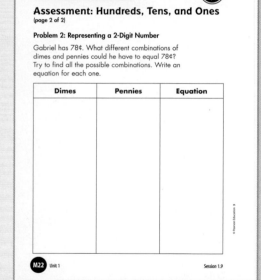

▲ Resource Masters, M22

"We started at 153 on the 200 chart because we know that 153¢ is the same as $1.53. We jumped 40 spaces to get to 193, and then 7 more spaces to get to 200. 40 plus 7 is 47, so he needs 47¢ more."

141	142	143	144	145	146	147	148	149	150
151	152	153	154	155	146	157	158	159	160
161	162	163	164	165	166	167	168	169	170
171	172	173	174	175	176	177	178	179	180
181	182	183	184	185	186	187	188	189	190
191	192	193	194	195	196	197	198	199	200

ASSESSMENT ACTIVITY

40 MIN   INDIVIDUALS

Hundreds, Tens, and Ones

For the remainder of this session, students complete Assessment: Hundreds, Tens, and Ones (M21–M22). Students add 2-digit numbers and find the difference between their sum and 100. They also represent a 2-digit number as different combinations of 10s and 1s. This assessment addresses Benchmarks 3, 4, and 5. Remind students to show how they solved each problem.

When students finish, they can continue work on the Math Workshop activities from Session 1.7.

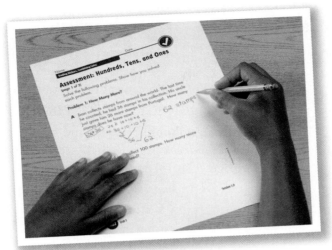

Professional Development

❶ **Teacher Note:** Assessment: Hundreds, Tens, and Ones, p. 153

In Problem 1, a student might combine the two quantities by starting with 36 and adding 26 in parts.

ONGOING ASSESSMENT: Observing Students at Work

Students add 2-digit numbers and find the difference between their sum and 100. They also represent a 2-digit number as different combinations of 10s and 1s.

Problem 1

- **Are students able to accurately solve the two-step problem, finding the sum of the numbers first and then the difference between that sum and 100?**❶

- **What strategies do students use to find the sum?** Do they break apart both numbers by place to add them? Do they add on one number in parts? Do they use combinations that they know make 100?

- **What strategies do they use to find the missing addend?** Do they add or subtract multiples of 10? Do they try to add or subtract to get numbers that are easy to work with (e.g., add 8 to 72 first to get to 80, which is easy to calculate with)?

Problem 2

- **Are students representing a 2-digit number as 10s and 1s?** Do their solutions demonstrate understanding of the equivalence of one 10 to ten 1s, two 10s to twenty 1s, and so on? Do they find all possible combinations of 10s and 1s for 78¢?

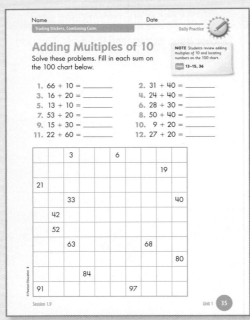

▲ Studenty Activity Book, p. 35

3 Daily Practice

 Daily Practice: For reinforcement of this unit's content, have students complete *Student Activity Book* page 35.

 Student Math Handbook: Students and families may use *Student Math Handbook* pages 7–8, 37–38 for reference and review. See pages 174–181 in the back of this unit.

Mathematical Emphases

The Base-Ten Number System Understanding the equivalence of one group and the units that comprise it

Math Focus Points

◆ Recognizing and demonstrating the equivalence of one 100 to ten 10s and of one 10 to ten 1s

◆ Recognizing and using coin equivalencies

◆ Finding different combinations of 100s, 10s, and 1s for a number and recognizing their equivalence (i.e. 1 hundred, 3 tens, and 7 ones equals 1 hundred, 2 tens, and 17 ones, or 13 tens and 7 ones)

Computational Fluency Adding and subtracting accurately and efficiently

Math Focus Points

◆ Learning/reviewing addition combinations up to $10 + 10$

◆ Using knowledge of place value to find pairs of 2-digit numbers that add to 100 or a number close to 100

◆ Using known pairs of 2-digit numbers that add to 100 to find related pairs that add to 100 or a number close to 100 (for example, $20 + 80 = 100$, so $22 + 78 = 100$)

◆ Finding the difference between a 2-digit number and 100

◆ Estimating the sums of 2-digit numbers by using knowledge of place value and known combinations

◆ Finding combinations of coins that equal $1.00

◆ Solving addition problems with 2-digit numbers by using strategies that involve breaking numbers apart by place or adding one number in parts

Working with 100

	Student Activity Book	Student Math Handbook	Professional Development: Read Ahead of Time
SESSION 2.1 p. 96			
Addition Combinations Students review the addition combinations up to 10 + 10 and identify the combinations they do not yet know fluently. They use knowledge of combinations they know to help them learn the unknown combinations.	36–38	16–19	• **Teacher Note:** Learning the Addition Combinations, p. 159
SESSION 2.2 p. 102			
Close to 100 Students use knowledge of place value and known combinations with sums of 100 (20 + 80, 25 + 75, 50 + 50, etc.) to find pairs of 2-digit numbers that add to 100 or close to 100.	39–40	13–15; G5	• **Dialogue Box:** Strategies for *Close to 100*, p. 172
SESSION 2.3 p. 109			
More or Less Than 100? Students are introduced to *More or Less,* a Ten-Minute Math activity in which they estimate the sums of 2-digit numbers. They continue work on finding pairs of 2-digit numbers that add to 100 and discuss their strategies.	41–44	13–15, 20–24	• **Part 4: Ten-Minute Math and Classroom Routines** in *Implementing Investigations in Grade 3:* More or Less? • **Teacher Note:** Does Order Matter In Addition?, p. 152
SESSION 2.4 p. 116			
Coin Combinations Students review coin equivalencies and find combinations of coins that equal $1.00.	45–48	37–38	• **Dialogue Box:** Strategies for *Make a Dollar,* p. 173

Ten-Minute Math See page 18 for an overview.

What's the Temperature?
- Thermometer; temperature chart; temperature graph

Practicing Place Value
- No materials needed

More or Less?
- No materials needed

Materials to Gather	Materials to Prepare
• **Envelopes** (2 per student)	• **M23–M28, Addition Cards** Make copies. (1 deck per student) Cut apart the cards and shuffle each deck before handing out. • **M29, Addition Combinations Practice** Make copies. (1 per student) • **M31–M32, Family Letter** Make copies. (1 per student) • **Chart: "Addition Card Categories"** Divide chart paper into six sections. Label to match the chart on *Student Activity Book* page 36.
• **T9, *Close to 100* Recording Sheet** 🖨 • **Cubes, in towers of 10** (10 towers per pair; as needed)	• **M30, *Close to 100*** Make copies. (as needed) • **M33–M35, Digit Cards** Make copies. (1 deck per 2–4 students) Cut apart the cards and remove the wild cards before handing out. • **M36, *Close to 100* Recording Sheet** Make copies. (1 per student, plus extras) • **Chart: "Ways to Make 100"** Divide chart paper into two columns, and label them "Ways to Make 10" and "Ways to Make 100." See page 103.
• **Blank transparency sheet** • **Chart: "Ways to Make 100"** • **Materials for *Close to 100*** (from Session 2.2)	
• **T10, Coins** 🖨 • **T15, *Make a Dollar* Recording Sheet** 🖨 • **Blank paper**	• **M4, 100 Chart** Make copies. (as needed) • **M38, *Make a Dollar*** Make copies. (as needed) • **M39–M42, Coin Cards** Make copies. (1 deck per pair) Cut apart the cards before handing out. • **M43, *Make a Dollar* Recording Sheet** Make copies. (1 per student, plus extras) • **T11–T14 Coin Cards** 🖨 Cut apart the transparency cards. • **Coin and Dollar Sets** Use the pennies, dimes, and dollars sets from Investigation 1, and add 20 nickels, 20 quarters, and 2 half dollars to each set. (1 set per pair) • **Chart: "Ways to Make A Dollar"** Label a sheet of chart paper "Ways to Make a Dollar."

🖨 Overhead Transparency

Working with 100, *continued*

	Student Activity Book	Student Math Handbook	Professional Development: Read Ahead of Time	
SESSION 2.5 p. 121				
Assessment: Addition Combinations Students are assessed on their fluency with addition combinations up to 10 + 10. In Math Workshop, they play games involving combinations that add to 100 or $1.00 and solve story problems.	49–50	20–24, 29, 30	• **Teacher Note:** Assessment: Addition	
SESSION 2.6 p. 125				
Story Problem Strategies Students discuss story problem strategies. In Math Workshop, they find combinations of 100 and $1.00; add and subtract multiples of 10s and 1s; and trade 100s, 10s, and 1s.	51–53	7–8, 13–15, 36		
SESSION 2.7 p. 133				
163 Stickers Students discuss the equivalence of different combinations of hundreds, tens, and ones for the same number. In Math Workshop, they continue finding combinations that add to 100 and $1.00 and solve story problems that involve finding equivalencies of 100s, 10s, and 1s.	55–57	7–8, 9		
SESSION 2.8 p. 139				
End-of-Unit Assessment Students complete assessment tasks that focus on addition, combinations that make 100, and place value.	59	7–8, 20–24, 36	• **Teacher Note:** End-of-Unit Assessment, p. 164	

Materials to Gather	Materials to Prepare
• **Materials for** *Make a Dollar* (from Session 2.4) • **Materials for** *Close to 100* (from Session 2.4)	• **M18, 200 Chart** Make copies. (as needed) • **M44, Assessment: Addition Combinations** Make copies. (1 per student) • **M45, Blank Addition Combinations** Make copies. (as needed; optional)
• **Cubes, in towers of 10** (as needed) • **Materials for** *Capture 5* (from Session 1.5) • **Materials for** *Make a Dollar* (from Session 2.5) • **Materials for** *Close to 100* (from Session 2.5)	• **M29, Addition Combinations Practice** Make copies. (1 per student) After you have had a chance to review students' work on this assessment, decide which addition combinations you will assign to individuals, small groups, or the class as a whole for homework, on the basis of assessment results in Session 2.5.
• **Cubes, in towers of 10** (as needed) • **Coin and Dollar Sets** (as needed; from Session 2.4) • **Materials for** *Capture 5* (from Session 1.5) • **Materials for** *Make a Dollar* (from Session 2.6) • **Materials for** *Close to 100* (from Session 2.6)	• **M12, 100 Grids** Make copies. (as needed) • **M18, 200 Chart** Make copies. (as needed) • **M29, Addition Combinations Practice** Make copies. (1 per student) Assign addition combinations according to students' needs, or let students choose the combinations they will work on.
	• **M46–M48, End-of-Unit Assessment** Make copies. (1 per student)

Addition Combinations

Math Focus Points

◆ Learning/reviewing addition combinations up to 10 + 10

Today's Plan		Materials
ACTIVITY **① Introducing Addition Card Categories and Clues**	30 MIN CLASS PAIRS	• *Student Activity Book,* p. 36 • M23–M28* • Chart: "Addition Card Categories"*
ACTIVITY **② Combinations I Know and Combinations I'm Working On**	30 MIN INDIVIDUALS	• M23–M28; M29* • Envelopes
SESSION FOLLOW-UP **③ Daily Practice and Homework**		• M29* • *Student Activity Book,* pp. 37–38 • *Student Math Handbook,* pp. 16–19 • M31–M32, Family Letter*

*See *Materials to Prepare,* p. 93.

Ten-Minute Math

Practicing Place Value: How Many 10s? Write 128 on the board, and ask students to practice saying it to a partner. Make sure all students can read, write, and say this number correctly.

If we had strips of 10 stickers, how many strips would there be to represent this number? (12)

How many single stickers? (8)

If I wanted to break up 128 so that there are 11 strips of 10, how many singles would there be? (18)

How many singles if there are 10 strips of 10? (28)

How many singles if there are 9 strips of 10? (38)

If time remains, pose similar problems using the number 136.

ACTIVITY

30 MIN | CLASS | PAIRS

1 Introducing Addition Card Categories and Clues

This activity helps you determine which students require practice with addition combinations, and helps identify the specific categories of combinations that these students need to practice. ❶

Distribute one set of prepared Addition Cards (M23–M28) to each student.

In Grade 2, you worked on learning your addition combinations up to 10 + 10. You made addition cards and wrote clues on them to help you learn the combinations you didn't yet know. We're going to use addition cards again this year so that you can continue to practice these combinations. Just like last year, you'll work on these combinations in categories. I'm going to give you a few minutes to sort your cards into six groups. You'll find these groups in your *Student Activity Book* on page 36.

Display the "Addition Card Categories" chart you prepared. Take a few minutes to make sure that students understand what each category means. Give an example of each, if necessary, and write the examples on the chart. Explain that any cards that do not fit in the first five categories go in the "Remaining Combinations" category.

Work with a partner to sort the addition cards. Then, in the chart on page 36, write the combinations that fit in each category.

A student gets ready to share the near doubles combinations he found with his addition cards.

Professional Development

❶ **Teacher Note:** Learning the Addition Combinations, p. 159

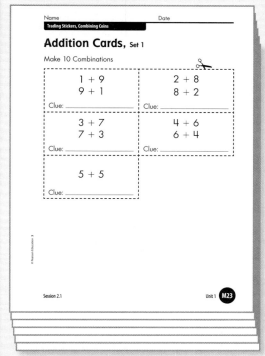

▲ **Resource Masters, M23–M28**

Name _____ Date _____

Trading Stickers, Combining Coins

Addition Card Categories

After sorting your addition cards into categories, write each combination in the correct space below.

For example, 9 + 1 = _____ will go in the space labeled *Make 10 Combinations*.

Make 10 Combinations	Doubles
Near Doubles (Doubles Plus or Minus 1)	Plus 10 Combinations
Plus 9 Combinations	Remaining Combinations

36 Unit 1   Session 2.1

▲ **Student Activity Book, p. 36**

❷ **Combination Categories** Students may list some of the addition combinations under more than one category. For example, 9 + 9 might be listed as a double as well as a plus 9 combination, and 5 + 5 might be listed as both a double and a make 10 combination. Acknowledge this possibility if it comes up in discussion. The purpose of classifying the combinations is simply to help students learn those they may still need to practice. It does not matter whether they put a particular combination in one or more than one category.

Give students 10–15 minutes to complete this task. Then, call them back together, and direct their attention to the "Doubles" category. Ask students to share the combinations they put in this category. List them on the class chart.❷

You probably know the answer to many of the doubles combinations, such as 3 + 3 or 5 + 5 or 10 + 10. Let's think about how to use the combinations you know to figure out the sums of the combinations you're not sure of. For example, doubles can help you with those combinations that are close to doubles. Is there a combination that you already know that might help you find the sum of 6 + 5?

Students might say:

"I can figure out 6 plus 5 because I know my doubles. I know that 5 plus 5 equals 10, so 6 plus 5 has to be one more than that. So 6 plus 5 equals 11."

"I used doubles, but I used 6 plus 6 equals 12. This problem is 6 plus 5, so the answer has to be one less, or 11."

When you work with your addition cards today, you're going to sort them into two piles: the combinations you know, and the combinations you are still working on. You'll write clues to help you learn the combinations you don't yet know. For example, if you used 5 plus 5 to find the sum of 6 plus 5, you can write that as a clue on the 6 plus 5 card. If you used 6 plus 6, you can write that clue on the card.

Quickly sketch two 5 + 6 and 6 + 5 addition cards on the board, and show students where to write these clues.

| 5 + 6 |
| 6 + 5 |
| Clue: Think 5 + 5 add 1 |

| 5 + 6 |
| 6 + 5 |
| Clue: 6 + 6 −1 |

Let's look at the +9 combinations. What are some combinations that you put in this category? Is there a combination that you already know that might help you find the sum of 9 and 4?

Students might say:

"I can figure out 9 plus 4 because I know that 10 plus 4 equals 14. 9 is one less than 10, so 9 plus 4 has to be 13."

"I can take one from the 4 and give it to the 9 to make it a 10. Then I have 10 + 3, which is 13."❸

Algebra Note

❸ **Using Related or Equivalent Problems for Addition Combinations** Underlying these strategies are generalizations. Encourage students to state the general principle and to show how they know this principle works for 9 and 4 and for other pairs of numbers. See Algebra Connections in This Unit (p. 16) for more information.

So you used a +10 combination, 10 + 4, to figure out the sum of a +9 combination, 9 + 4. That's the clue you would write on your card if 9 + 4 is a combination you need to work on.

Draw this card on the board, and show students where to write the clue.

9 + 4
4 + 9
Clue: $\underline{10 + 4 - 1}$

ACTIVITY

30 MIN INDIVIDUALS

② Combinations I Know and Combinations I'm Working On

Write "Combinations I Know" and "Combinations I'm Working On" on the board. Distribute two envelopes to each student, and tell them to write one label on each envelope. Then tell students to mix up their addition cards and put them back into one pile. Explain that their task is to sort the cards into 2 piles: the combinations they know and those they are still working on.

If you can say the answer to a combination in a couple of seconds, you can put that card right into your "Combinations I Know" envelope. If it takes you a little while to figure out the answer, put the card in a "Combinations I'm Working On" pile.

Name _____ Date _____

Trading Stickers, Combining Coins

Addition Combinations Practice

___ + ___ =
___ + ___ =
Clue: _____

___ + ___ =
___ + ___ =
Clue: _____

___ + ___ =
___ + ___ =
Clue: _____

___ + ___ =
___ + ___ =
Clue: _____

___ + ___ =
___ + ___ =
Clue: _____

___ + ___ =
___ + ___ =
Clue: _____

Sessions 2.1, 2.6, 2.7   Unit 1 **M29**

▲ **Resource Masters, M29**

Teaching Note

❹ **Assessing What Students Know** Students will continue to practice the combinations in their "working on" piles throughout the rest of this unit and, if necessary, in subsequent units. Go through students' "working on" envelopes before the next math session. When you have determined the combinations that each student needs to work on, you can decide how much practice each student will need. This practice can then be assigned as additional homework, as a Math Workshop activity, or as something students work on when they have a few minutes after completing another activity.

When you have a pile of combinations you still need to practice, you'll write a clue on each card to help you find the sum, just as we did as a group with the near-double and +9 combinations.

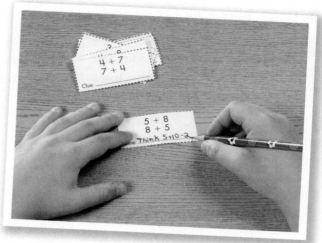

A student writes clues on the cards for combinations he still needs to practice.

Students work on this activity for the next 20–25 minutes. About 5 minutes before the end of the session, distribute copies of the Addition Combinations Practice sheet (M29). Tell students to choose 6 combinations from their "working on" piles that they want to practice at home, and to write those combinations on the blank cards on this sheet.

At the end of the session, have students place all their "working on" cards in the envelope with that label and write their name on the envelope. Collect these so you can review the work students need.❹ Let the class know that in a few more days (Session 2.5), you will be assessing how well they know these combinations.

ONGOING ASSESSMENT: Observing Students at Work

Students identify addition combinations they do not yet know fluently and select known combinations as clues to help learn them.

- **Which combinations do students know fluently?**

- **Do they understand and use the relationships between the combinations they know and those with which they are not yet fluent?** For example, do they use knowledge of doubles to help them solve near-doubles (doubles plus or minus 1)?

DIFFERENTIATION: Supporting the Range of Learners

Intervention If some students have trouble thinking of clues for their "working on" cards, sit with them to go through the combinations they know. Help them relate these combinations to the ones they are still working on. For example, if a student knows make-10 combinations, you might say:

I see you're not sure about the sum of 8 + 3. Is there a make-10 combination close to this that might help you?

Most students are likely to have a relatively small number of combinations in their "working on" piles. Students who have many cards in this pile can be assigned combinations to practice at home in groups of six at a time, using additional copies of Addition Combinations Practice (M29). Help these students choose combinations in the same category to practice together.

ELL If you feel an English Language Learner is struggling with saying names of numbers, you can partner him or her with a student who is fluent in English. Have the fluent English speaker say everything aloud while the English Language Learner acts as a checker. Then have students reverse roles.

SESSION FOLLOW-UP

③ Daily Practice and Homework

 Daily Practice: For reinforcement of this unit's content, have students complete *Student Activity Book* page 37.

 Homework: Have students take home the combinations they filled in on the Addition Combinations Practice sheet (M29). Suggest that they cut apart the cards at home. On *Student Activity Book* page 38, students record how they worked with a friend or family member on the six combinations they have chosen.

 Student Math Handbook: Students and families may use *Student Math Handbook* pages 16–19 for reference and review. See pages 174–181 in the back of this unit.

 Family Letter: Send home copies of the Family Letter (M31–M32).

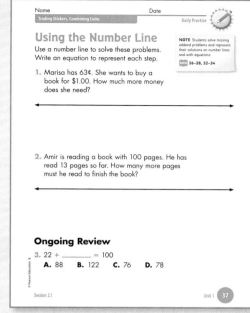

Using the Number Line

Use a number line to solve these problems. Write an equation to represent each step.

NOTE Students solve missing addend problems and represent their solutions on number lines and with equations.
26–28, 32–34

1. Marisa has 63¢. She wants to buy a book for $1.00. How much more money does she need?

2. Amir is reading a book with 100 pages. He has read 13 pages so far. How many more pages must he read to finish the book?

Ongoing Review

3. 22 + _____ = 100
   A. 88   **B.** 122   **C.** 76   **D.** 78

Session 2.1   Unit 1   37

▲ Student Activity Book, p. 37

Practice with Addition Combinations

NOTE Students are reviewing the addition combinations (addition "facts") they worked on in Grade 2 and practicing those they don't yet know. Ask your child to explain how the clues help with these combinations.
16–19

1. Which addition combinations are you practicing?
   _____ _____
   _____ _____
   _____ _____

2. Write two addition combinations that are hard for you, and explain what helps you remember them.
   Addition combination: _____
   What helps me:
   _____
   _____

   Addition combination: _____
   What helps me:
   _____
   _____

3. How did you practice your addition combinations? Who helped you?
   _____
   _____
   _____

38   Unit 1   Session 2.1

▲ Student Activity Book, p. 38

Close to 100

Math Focus Points

◆ Using knowledge of place value to find pairs of 2-digit numbers that add to 100 or a number close to 100

◆ Using known pairs of 2-digit numbers that add to 100 to find related pairs that add to 100 or a number close to 100 (for example, 20 + 80 = 100, so 22 + 78 = 100)

◆ Finding the difference between a 2-digit number and 100

Today's Plan		Materials
ACTIVITY ❶ Introducing *Close to 100*	🕐 20 MIN 👥 CLASS	• M30*; M33–M35* • T9 🖨 • Chart: "Ways to Make 100"* • Cubes, in towers of 10
ACTIVITY ❷ *Close to 100*	🕐 40 MIN 👥 PAIRS 👥 GROUPS	• *Student Activity Book,* p. 39 • M33–M35; M36*
SESSION FOLLOW-UP ❸ Daily Practice		• *Student Activity Book,* p. 40 • *Student Math Handbook,* pp. 13–15; G5

*See *Materials to Prepare,* p. 93.

Ten-Minute Math

Practicing Place Value: How Many 10s? Write 143 on the board, and ask students to practice saying it to a partner. Make sure all students can read, write, and say this number correctly.

If we had strips of 10 stickers, how many strips would there be to represent this number? (14)
How many single stickers? (3)

If I wanted to break up 143 so that there are 13 singles, how many strips of 10 would there be? (13)

How many strips of 10 if there are 23 singles? (12) How many strips of 10 if there are 33 singles? (11)

If time remains, pose similar problems using the number 157.

ACTIVITY

Introducing *Close to 100*

20 MIN   CLASS

Distribute 100 cubes (in towers of 10) to each pair of students. Begin the session by having students share the make-10 addition combinations that use 2 addends. List them in order on the "Ways to Make 100" chart you prepared ahead of time.

Ways to Make 100	
Ways to Make 10	Ways to Make 100
1 + 9	
2 + 8	
3 + 7	
4 + 6	
5 + 5	
6 + 4	
7 + 3	
8 + 2	
9 + 1	

How can you use these make-10 combinations to figure out combinations that make 100? For example, can 2 + 8 = 10 help you figure out what to add to 20 to make 100? [Write 20 + _____ = 100 on the board.] Work on this with the person next to you for a couple of minutes. Use cubes to show your answer.

Ask a pair of students to use cubes to show what they added to 20 to make 100, and to explain how they know they have 100.

So you added 8 towers of 10 to the 2 towers of 10 you started with. How many towers of 10 did you have then? How many cubes was that in all? How do you know? How did 2 ones plus 8 ones, help you with 2 tens plus 8 tens?

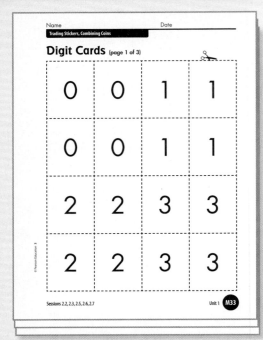

▲ Resource Masters, M33–M35

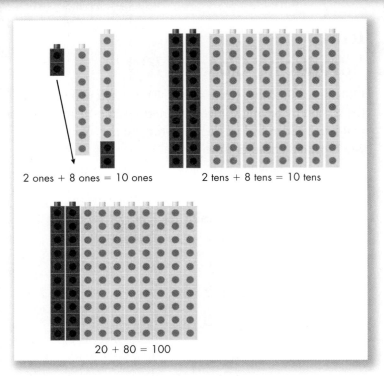

2 ones + 8 ones = 10 ones   2 tens + 8 tens = 10 tens

20 + 80 = 100

We know that 20 plus 80 equals 100. What other pairs of multiples of 10 can we add together to make 100? Work with your partner on this.

Give students a few minutes to work on this. Then, as students share combinations, ask them to model with cubes and explain how they know that they have 100. Record the combinations in order next to the make-10 combinations.

Ways to Make 100	
Ways to Make 10	Ways to Make 100
1 + 9	10 + 90
2 + 8	20 + 80
3 + 7	30 + 70
4 + 6	40 + 60
5 + 5	50 + 50
6 + 4	60 + 40
7 + 3	70 + 30
8 + 2	80 + 20
9 + 1	90 + 10

Look at our chart. What patterns do you notice? What's the same about the combinations that equal 10 and those that equal 100? What's different?

Students are likely to comment that the tens digits of the combinations that make 100 are the same as the ones digits of the combinations that make 10: 2 plus 8 equals 10 and 20 plus 80 equals 100; 6 plus 4 equals 10 and 60 plus 40 equals 100, and so on. However, the digits in the combinations that make 10 are ones, and the corresponding digits in the combinations that make 100 are tens.

Why do you think this pattern occurs? For example, why do 2 ones plus 8 ones equal 10, and 2 tens plus 8 tens equal 100?

Students might say:

"2 plus 8 equals 10, so 2 tens plus 8 tens equal 10 tens, and 10 tens equal 100. Anytime you make 10 tens, you make 100."

On our chart, we just listed all the ways to make 100 by adding 2 multiples of 10. This will be helpful for a new game you're going to play, called *Close to 100.* Now we're going to learn that game. To play the game, you will need a set of Digit Cards. Each player also needs a *Close to 100* Recording Sheet.

Make available one or more copies of the rules for *Close to 100* (M30). Show students a deck of Digit Cards (M33–M35), and display the transparent *Close to 100* Recording Sheet (T9).

For the first round of the game, you deal out 6 cards. Suppose that these are the 6 cards you get. [Quickly sketch the following six digit cards on the board:]

In this game, you put 2 cards together to make 2-digit numbers, such as 55 or 97. Your goal is to make a pair of 2-digit numbers that add to a sum of 100, or as close to 100 as possible.

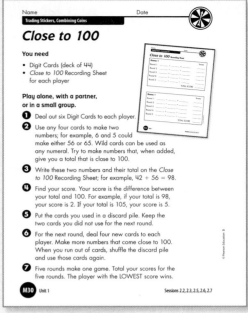

▲ **Resource Masters, M30**

▲ **Student Activity Book, p. 39**
Resource Masters, M36; T9

Math Note

❶ Scoring the Game In this basic version of the game, the score is the difference between the sum of the two numbers and 100, whether the sum is more or less than 100. For example, 98 and 102 both have a score of 2. In a later unit, students will learn a variation of this game with positive and negative scoring.

Teaching Note

❷ Encouraging Cooperation Stress the importance of taking turns and helping each other find the combination closest to 100. Some teachers suggest that students wait until a player's turn has come up to deal out the new cards for that turn. This helps both players focus on the cards of the player whose turn is in progress, and fosters more cooperation and discussion during the game.

Tell students to use these six cards to make two 2-digit numbers that add to 100 or close to 100. Students work with a partner to generate possible combinations. Suggest that they refer to the chart "Ways to Make 100" to help them think of good combinations. After a few minutes, record some of their ideas.

$$59 + 37 = 96 \qquad 47 + 53 = 100$$
$$49 + 53 = 102 \qquad 53 + 54 = 107$$

When you play *Close to 100,* your score for each round is the difference between your number and 100, or how far your answer is from 100. What would be the score for each of these combinations? In other words, how far from 100 is each of these sums?❶

Record the score for each equation students suggested. For example:

$$59 + 37 = 96 \quad \text{Score: } 4$$

In this game, your goal is to get the *lowest* score. Which combination of numbers from these six cards gives you the best score?

Record this equation and score on the transparent *Close to 100* Recording Sheet (T9).

Remove the 4 cards you used, deal out 4 more (sketching these on the board), and play one or two more rounds with the class to demonstrate the rules.

Highlight the following rules as you play:

- Each player has 6 cards to choose from.

- After each round, discard the 4 cards used and draw 4 new cards before your next turn.

- You must use exactly 4 cards. For example, students cannot use 93 + 7 unless they have a 0 and can make 93 + 07.

- After five rounds, students total their scores. The lowest score wins.

ACTIVITY

❷ *Close to 100*

Students play *Close to 100* in groups of 2–4. Each group will need one set of Digit Cards (M33–M35), with the wild cards removed, and each student will need the individual scoring sheet on *Student Activity Book* page 39.❷ Make available extra copies of *Close to 100* Recording Sheet (M36) as needed.

Professional Development

Dialogue Box: Strategies for *Close to 100,* p. 172

Students add 2-digit numbers as they play
Close to 100.

ONGOING ASSESSMENT: Observing Students at Work

Students find pairs of 2-digit numbers with sums equal to or close to 100.

- **Are students trying combinations randomly, or are they considering combinations that they know make 100 (such as 50 + 50 or 30 + 70) and using them to find other combinations that are equal to or close to 100?**

- **Do students consider the sum of the tens digits when picking two numbers?** For example, do they recognize that if they have a number in the 20s, they will need the second number to be in the 70s or 80s to be close to 100?

- **Are students looking for a way to make a combination of 90 with the tens digits and 10 with the ones digits?**

Observe the strategies that students are using as they play the game.❸

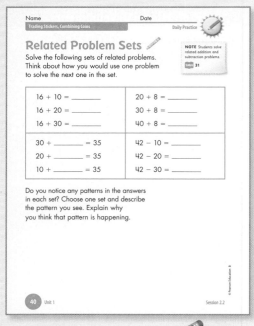

▲ **Student Activity Book, p. 40**

DIFFERENTIATION: Supporting the Range of Learners

Intervention In this first opportunity to play *Close to 100*, most students will be working on learning the rules to the game. Although some students will soon invent strategies for finding combinations close to 100, others may have difficulty finding a starting place. If a student is having difficulty, make one 2-digit number from his or her cards that you know can be paired with another to get close to 100. Ask what number the student could make to add to yours to get as close to 100 as possible. As the student works, pose situations and questions like the following:

- I just made the number 28. What multiple of 10 is that close to? What would you add to 30 to get to exactly 100? Can you make a number close to that with your cards?

- What are some combinations that you know make 100? Are there any numbers that you could make with the cards in your hand that would be close to the combinations that you know?

ELL You may want to pair students so that English Language Learners can work with native speakers to help them understand the rules.

SESSION FOLLOW-UP
3 Daily Practice

 Daily Practice: For reinforcement of this unit's content, have students complete *Student Activity Book* page 40.

Student Math Handbook: Students and families may use *Student Math Handbook* pages 13–15 and G5 for reference and review. See pages 174–181 in the back of this unit.

More or Less Than 100?

Math Focus Points

◆ Estimating the sums of 2-digit numbers by using knowledge of place value and known combinations

◆ Using knowledge of place value to find pairs of 2-digit numbers that add to 100 or a number close to 100

◆ Using known pairs of 2-digit numbers that add to 100 to find related pairs that add to 100 or a number close to 100 (for example, $20 + 80 = 100$, so $22 + 78 = 100$)

Today's Plan		Materials
1 ACTIVITY **More or Less Than 100?** 15 MIN · CLASS · PAIRS		• Blank transparency sheet
2 MATH WORKSHOP **Adding to 100** **2A** *Close to 100* **2B** Problems for *Close to 100* 30 MIN		**2A** • M36* • Digit Cards (from Session 2.2) • Chart: "Ways to Make 100" (from Session 2.2) **2B** • *Student Activity Book,* pp. 41–42
3 DISCUSSION **Strategies for *Close to 100*** 15 MIN · CLASS		• *Student Activity Book,* p. 41 (completed)
4 SESSION FOLLOW-UP **Daily Practice and Homework**		• *Student Activity Book,* pp. 43–44 • *Student Math Handbook,* pp. 13–15, 20–24

*See *Materials to Prepare,* p. 93.

Ten-Minute Math

Note: The Ten-Minute Math activity for this unit, *More or Less?,* is introduced in this session. Plan to do today's Ten-Minute Math sometime after math class, if possible.

More or Less? Write the problem $0.35 + $0.63 on the board. Students estimate the sum and decide if it is more or less than $1.00. Select students to share their strategies.

What did you pay attention to when you looked at these numbers?

Did you use combinations you know that equal 100 or $1.00 to help you?

If time remains, pose similar problems such as 25¢ + 78¢ and 13¢ + 40¢ + 45¢.

Professional Development

❶ **Part 4: Ten-Minute Math and Classroom Routines** in *Implementing Investigations in Grade 3:* More or Less?

ACTIVITY

① More or Less Than 100?

15 MIN CLASS PAIRS

More or Less is a Ten-Minute Math activity that students will be doing for the rest of this unit and at other times throughout the year.❶

I'm going to show you an addition problem, but don't figure out the exact answer. Just think about whether the sum is more or less than 100.

Write the following expression on a blank transparency, and show it for about 20 seconds before covering it or turning off the projector.

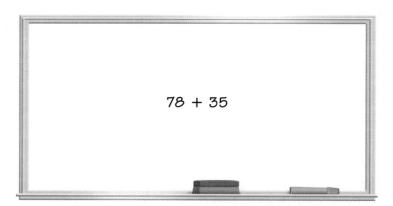

78 + 35

Give students a few minutes to talk about this problem with a partner. Then ask a few volunteers to answer the question and explain their thinking.

Students might say:

 "I know that 70 plus 30 equals 100. But 78 is more than 70 and 35 is more than 30, so the answer has to be more than 100."

 "I looked at the digits in the tens place, and 7 plus 3 equals 10, so 70 plus 30 equals 100. The ones digits would make the answer more than 100."

 "78 is almost 80. I know that 80 plus 20 equals 100. 35 is more than 20, so the answer is more than 100."

Now ask students to solve the problem either mentally, or using paper and pencil. Record 2 or 3 strategies for the solution on the board. For example, a student might solve it this way:

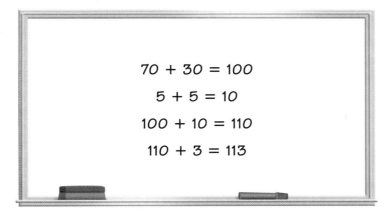

70 + 30 = 100

5 + 5 = 10

100 + 10 = 110

110 + 3 = 113

Finding the exact answer is an optional part of this activity, depending on time and the difficulty of the problem. Since the focus is on estimation, ask students to use the exact answer to consider how well they estimated.

Let's look at another problem and do the same thing. Remember, at our first look, you don't have to figure out the exact answer. Just tell us if it's more or less than 100.

Write 37 + 61 on the transparency and repeat the procedure above, again asking students to explain their reasoning about whether the answer is more or less than 100.

As students share responses, listen for ways in which they use knowledge of place value and combinations of 10 and 100 to answer this question.

Students might say:

 "I looked at the tens place: 3 tens and 6 tens equal 9 tens, or 90, so I knew I would need a total of 10 in the ones place to make 100. Then 7 plus 1 is less than 10, so the answer is less than 100."

As before, have students find the exact answer to this problem, and compare the exact answer to their estimates.

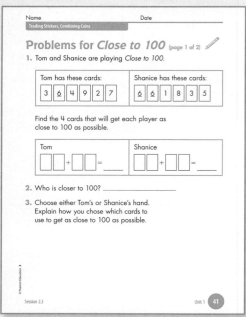

Name _____ Date _____

Trading Stickers, Combining Coins

Problems for *Close to 100* (page 1 of 2)

1. Tom and Shanice are playing *Close to 100*.

Tom has these cards:	Shanice has these cards:
3 6 4 9 2 7	6 6 1 8 3 5

Find the 4 cards that will get each player as close to 100 as possible.

Tom	Shanice
☐☐ + ☐☐ = ___	☐☐ + ☐☐ = ___

2. Who is closer to 100? _____

3. Choose either Tom's or Shanice's hand. Explain how you chose which cards to use to get as close to 100 as possible.

Session 2.3   Unit 1 **41**

▲ **Student Activity Book, p. 41**

Name _____ Date _____

Trading Stickers, Combining Coins

Problems for *Close to 100* (page 2 of 2)

Solve each problem, and record your strategy by using equations. If you use 100 grids or number lines to solve the problems, show how you used those tools.

4. Bianca is playing *Close to 100*. She makes the number 57 with her cards and says, "I can get to 100 exactly." What 2-digit number will she make to get to 100 exactly? Explain how you know.

5. Caleb is playing *Close to 100*. He makes the number 31 with his cards and says, "I can get to 100, too." What 2-digit number will he make to get to 100 exactly? Explain how you know.

42 Unit 1   Session 2.3

▲ **Student Activity Book, p. 42**

ONGOING ASSESSMENT: Observing Students at Work

Students estimate the sums of addition problems to determine whether the sums are more or less than 100.

- **What strategies do students use to estimate the sums of these problems?** Do they use knowledge of combinations that add to 100? Do they use knowledge of place value to determine whether the sums are more or less than 100?

MATH WORKSHOP

② Adding to 100

30 MIN

Students play *Close to 100* and solve problems on *Student Activity Book* pages 41–42. Remind students that they may refer to the class chart, "Ways to Make 100" as they do the Math Workshop activities. Make sure that all students complete problems 1–3 on page 41 so that they will be prepared for the discussion at the end of this session.

As students work, identify those who use the following strategies. You will be asking them to share these strategies during the discussion.

- Using known combinations that add to 100 to find other combinations that add to 100 or a number close to 100

- Considering the sum of the tens digits when picking two numbers

- Making a combination that adds to 90 with the tens digits and 10 with the ones digits

. . . .

2A *Close to 100*

PAIRS

For complete details about this activity, see Session 2.2, pages 103–108.

2B Problems for *Close to 100*

INDIVIDUALS

Students solve problems on *Student Activity Book* pages 41–42. In these problems for *Close to 100*, they make pairs of 2-digit numbers that add to 100 or close to 100.

ONGOING ASSESSMENT: Observing Students at Work

Students find pairs of 2-digit numbers that equal 100 or close to 100.

Refer to the questions for *Close to 100* in Session 2.2, page 107.

DIFFERENTIATION: Supporting the Range of Learners

Refer to the suggestions for *Close to 100* in Session 2.2, page 108.

DISCUSSION

③ Strategies for *Close to 100*

15 MIN   CLASS

Math Focus Points for Discussion

◆ Using knowledge of place value to find pairs of 2-digit numbers that add to 100 or a number close to 100

◆ Using known pairs of 2-digit numbers that add to 100 to find related pairs that add to 100 or a number close to 100 (for example: $20 + 80 = 100$, so $22 + 78 = 100$)

For this discussion, students keep their *Student Activity Book* open to page 41. Focus attention on Tom's hand, and begin the discussion with one of the students whose strategy you wish to highlight.❷

Professional Development

❷ **Dialogue Box:** Strategies for *Close to 100,* p. 172

Differentiation

❸ **English Language Learners:** To make the discussion more meaningful to English Language Learners, write numbers and equations on the board as students say them in their explanations. If English Language Learners lack the language to share their strategies aloud, encourage them to write the numbers and equations they used on the board. As the students write, you can put their strategies into words for them.

Let's look at Tom's cards on page 41 and talk about some of the strategies you are using to play *Close to 100.* [Keisha,] I saw that you used a combination you already knew. Can you explain your strategy of using a known combination?❸

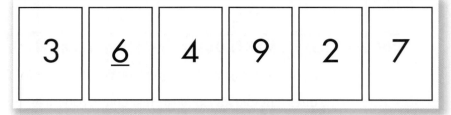

Students might say:

 "The equation I made was 76 + 24 = 100. I know that 75 + 25 = 100, but I couldn't make either of those numbers. I saw that I could make 76, so I knew that I had to make one less than 25 to get to exactly 100."

So [Keisha] used the known combination of [25 + 75 = 100] and then made numbers close to that. Did anyone else use a known combination?

I saw that [Arthur] used a strategy of first looking for digits to use in the tens place. Can you tell us what you did? . . . Did anyone else use the same strategy?

Students might say:

 "I wrote 62 + 37 = 99. I looked for two numbers in the tens place that would get me to 90. I know that 60 + 30 = 90. I looked for two numbers in the ones place that would equal 10, but the closest I could get was 9 with 2 + 7."

 "I did almost the same thing. I picked 6 and 3 for the tens place because I know that 60 + 30 = 90. Then I picked 7 and 2 because they got me close to 10. The numbers I made were 67 + 32 = 99. My numbers were almost the same as Arthur's."

As students play *Close to 100* and share strategies, they may notice that equations such as 62 + 37 and 67 + 32 result in the same sum, as do 27 + 73 and 77 + 23. If students make this observation, ask them to think about why this happens and whether they can always interchange the two digits in the tens place or the two digits in the ones place and still have the same sum.

If this observation does not come up, introduce the idea with the following expressions:

$$73 + 27 \qquad 77 + 23$$

Look at these two addition combinations. What do you notice about them? How are they the same? How are they different? What's the sum of each one? Do you think that you'll always get the same sum if you switch the digits in the ones place? Think about this more next time you play *Close to 100.* ❹ ❺

Professional Development

❹ **Teacher Note:** Does Order Matter in Addition?, p. 152

Algebra Note

❺ **Does Order Matter in Addition?** Asking students to notice regularities in the arithmetic expressions they encounter, supports their ability to state and prove generalizations. Ask students to generate other examples (for instance, 63 + 36 = 66 + 33) and to explain why this generalization about order of digits is true.

SESSION FOLLOW-UP
Daily Practice and Homework

 Daily Practice: For reinforcement of this unit's content, have students complete *Student Activity Book* page 43.

 Homework: Students use the sets of 6 Digit Cards pictured on *Student Activity Book* page 44 to make pairs of 2-digit numbers whose sum is 100 or close to 100.

 Student Math Handbook: Students and families may use *Student Math Handbook* pages 13–15, 20–24 for reference and review. See pages 174–181 in the back of this unit.

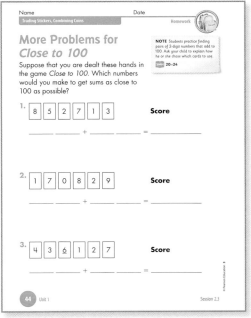

Name ___ Date ___
Trading Stickers, Combining Coins Homework

More Problems for *Close to 100*

Suppose that you are dealt these hands in the game *Close to 100*. Which numbers would you make to get sums as close to 100 as possible?

NOTE Students practice finding pairs of 2-digit numbers that add to 100. Ask your child to explain how he or she chose which cards to use. 20–24

1. | 8 | 5 | 2 | 7 | 1 | 3 | **Score**

___ ___ + ___ ___ = ___

2. | 1 | 7 | 0 | 8 | 2 | 9 | **Score**

___ ___ + ___ ___ = ___

3. | 4 | 3 | 6 | 1 | 2 | 7 | **Score**

___ ___ + ___ ___ = ___

44 Unit 1   Session 2.3

▲ **Student Activity Book, p. 44**

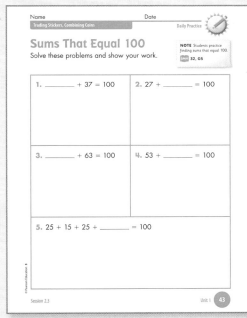

Name ___ Date ___
Trading Stickers, Combining Coins Daily Practice

Sums That Equal 100
Solve these problems and show your work.

NOTE Students practice finding sums that equal 100. 32, GS

1. ___ + 37 = 100   2. 27 + ___ = 100

3. ___ + 63 = 100   4. 53 + ___ = 100

5. 25 + 15 + 25 + ___ = 100

Session 2.3   Unit 1 43

▲ **Student Activity Book, p. 43**

Coin Combinations

Math Focus Points

◆ Finding combinations of coins that equal $1.00

◆ Recognizing and demonstrating the equivalence of one 100 to ten 10s and of one 10 to ten 1s

◆ Recognizing and using coin equivalencies

Vocabulary

quarter
nickel

Today's Plan		Materials
ACTIVITY **①** **Combinations to Make a Dollar**	20 MIN CLASS PAIRS	• T10 • Chart: "Ways to Make a Dollar"* • Coin and Dollar Sets*; blank paper
ACTIVITY **②** **Introducing** *Make a Dollar*	10 MIN CLASS	• M38*; T11–T14*
ACTIVITY **③** *Make a Dollar*	30 MIN PAIRS	• *Student Activity Book*, p. 45 • M4*; M39–M42*; M43* • Coin and Dollar Sets
SESSION FOLLOW-UP **④** **Daily Practice and Homework**		• *Student Activity Book*, pp. 46–48 • *Student Math Handbook*, pp. 37–38

*See *Materials to Prepare*, p. 93.

Ten-Minute Math

More or Less? Write the problem $0.42 + $0.55 on the board. Students estimate the sum and decide if it is more or less than $1.00. Select students to share their strategies.

What did you pay attention to when you looked at these numbers?

Did you use combinations you know that equal 100 or $1.00 to help you?

If time remains, pose similar problems such as $0.25 + $0.65 + $0.20 and 85¢ + 18¢.

ACTIVITY

Combinations to Make a Dollar

20 MIN   CLASS   PAIRS

Begin this session by briefly reviewing coin values and equivalencies, using the transparency of Coins (T10).

Which coin is worth 5¢? Which coin is worth 25¢? Which coins could we put together to make 25¢? How much is the largest coin worth? Which coins could we combine to make 50¢?

Which coins could we combine to make a dollar? How can combinations that make 100 help you find combinations that make a dollar?

Display the prepared "Ways to Make a Dollar" chart, and list some of the combinations that students share. Write each combination as an equation, sometimes using decimal notation and sometimes using the cent sign. Students should become comfortable with both ways to notate money. Point out that you have used two different notations to show the money amounts. The numbers before the decimal point show how many dollars, and the numbers after the decimal point show how many cents.

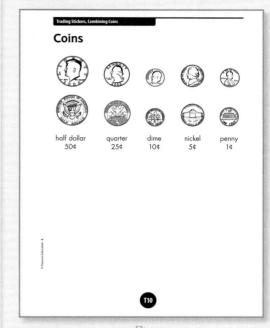

Coins

half dollar 50¢	quarter 25¢	dime 10¢	nickel 5¢	penny 1¢

T10

▲ **Transparencies, T10**

Ways to Make a Dollar

$0.50 + $0.50 = $1.00

$0.25 + $0.75 = $1.00

$0.53 + $0.47 = $1.00

10¢ + 10¢ + 80¢ = $1.00

$0.30 + $0.70 = $1.00

$0.60 + $0.40 = $1.00

64¢ + 36¢ = $1.00

Distribute Coin and Dollar sets to each pair of students. For about 10 minutes, pairs use these to generate combinations of coins that add to a dollar. They write these combinations on blank paper, making a list of combinations for reference in the next activity. If time allows, add a few of their combinations to the "Ways to Make a Dollar" chart.

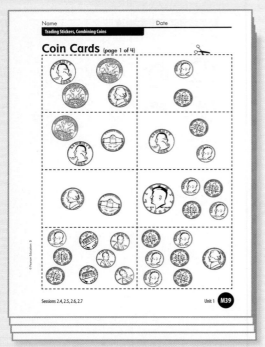

▲ Resource Masters, M39–M42

ONGOING ASSESSMENT: Observing Students at Work

Students find combinations of coins that equal a dollar.

- **Do students know coin names, values, and basic equivalencies?**

- **Do students use knowledge of the equivalence of 1 ten and 10 ones to find multiple solutions?** For example, do they reason that 10 dimes equal 1 dollar, so 9 dimes plus 10 pennies equal 1 dollar, 8 dimes and 20 pennies equal 1 dollar, and so on?

- **Do students use knowledge of other coin equivalencies to find different combinations that make a dollar?** For example, if they know that $0.50 + $0.50 = $1.00, do they use coins that equal $0.50—for example, 1 quarter, 2 dimes, and 1 nickel—to come up with another combination (50¢ + 25¢ + 10¢ + 10¢ + 5¢ = $1.00)?

DIFFERENTIATION: Supporting the Range of Learners

Intervention If some students are having difficulty with the activity, suggest that they find combinations to make 25¢ or 50¢ before moving on to combinations that make $1.00. These students can use additional time to work with the Coin and Dollar sets outside of math time.

ACTIVITY
2 Introducing *Make a Dollar*

10 MIN   CLASS

Display 8 cards from the transparent Coin Cards (M39–M42). Be sure to show at least two pairs of cards that combine to make a dollar.

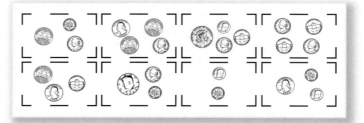

We are going to learn a new game called *Make a Dollar.* You will use Coin Cards like these. The object of the game is to find pairs of Coin Cards that add together to make *exactly* one dollar. Can you find two groups of coins that together equal one dollar?

As students find pairs of cards with coins that add to a dollar, demonstrate how to record these combinations on the *Make a Dollar* Recording Sheet (T15). Remove the cards that make the combination, and replace them with new cards.

Make available the rules for *Make a Dollar* (M38). Play one or two more rounds with the class to make sure that students understand the rules of the game.

ACTIVITY

3 Make a Dollar

30 MIN PAIRS

Distribute a prepared deck of Coin Cards (M39–M42) to each pair. Students play *Make a Dollar* with partners, finding pairs of Coin Cards that add to a dollar. They write the combinations they find on the recording sheet on *Student Activity Book* page 45. Remind students that they may refer to the "Ways to Make a Dollar" chart as they play.

Students work in pairs to find combinations of Coin Cards that equal a dollar.

ONGOING ASSESSMENT: Observing Students at Work

Students find combinations of coins that equal a dollar.

- **How do students determine the amounts on each card?** Do they recognize some combinations of coins? Do they add like coins first? Do they count on?

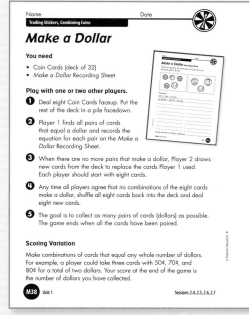

▲ **Resource Masters, M38**

❶ **Dialogue Box:** Strategies for *Make a Dollar*, p. 173

Make a Dollar Recording Sheet

Write an equation for each pair of cards that you find that add to $1.00.

Example:
45¢ + 55¢ = $1.00
(or $0.45 + $0.55 = $1.00)

Score (number of dollars collected): _____

▲ **Student Activity Book, p. 45;**
Resource Masters, M43; T15

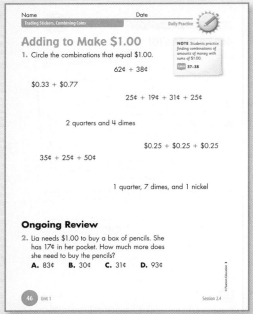

▲ Student Activity Book, p. 46

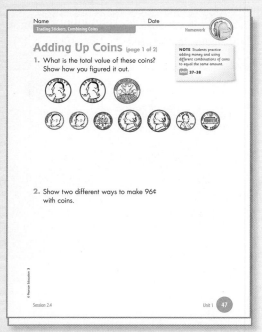

▲ Student Activity Book, pp. 47–48

- **What strategies do students use to find pairs of cards that add to a dollar?** Do they total the individual cards first and then look for known combinations? Do they choose one card and then determine how much more is needed? How do they make that determination?

As you observe students, ask some of the following questions to learn more about their thinking and to help them develop strategies:

- How much money is on this card? How did you add up the coins?

- I see that you have one card that is worth [60 cents]. How much more money do you need to make exactly one dollar? What coins might equal that amount?

- Are there any combinations that make one dollar, which you "just know" without adding the coins?

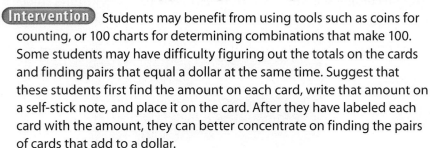

DIFFERENTIATION: Supporting the Range of Learners

Intervention Students may benefit from using tools such as coins for counting, or 100 charts for determining combinations that make 100. Some students may have difficulty figuring out the totals on the cards and finding pairs that equal a dollar at the same time. Suggest that these students first find the amount on each card, write that amount on a self-stick note, and place it on the card. After they have labeled each card with the amount, they can better concentrate on finding the pairs of cards that add to a dollar.

SESSION FOLLOW-UP

4 Daily Practice and Homework

 Daily Practice: For reinforcement of this unit's content, have students complete *Student Activity Book* page 46.

 Homework: Students solve addition and subtraction problems about money on *Student Activity Book* pages 47–48.

 Student Math Handbook: Students and families may use *Student Math Handbook* pages 37–38 for reference and review. See pages 174–181 in the back of this unit.

Assessment: Addition Combinations

Math Focus Points

◆ Finding combinations of coins that equal $1.00

◆ Using knowledge of place value to find pairs of 2-digit numbers that add to 100 or a number close to 100

◆ Solving addition problems with 2-digit numbers by using strategies that involve breaking numbers apart by place or adding one number in parts

Today's Plan		Materials
① MATH WORKSHOP **Adding to 100 and Story Problems** **①A** Assessment: Addition Combinations **①B** *Make a Dollar* **①C** Story Problems **①D** *Close to 100*	🕐 **60 MIN**	**①A** • M44* • M45* **①B** • M43* • Coin Cards (from Session 2.4) **①C** • *Student Activity Book,* p. 49 • M18* **①D** • M36* • Digit Cards (from Session 2.2)
② SESSION FOLLOW-UP **Daily Practice**		• *Student Activity Book,* p. 50 • *Student Math Handbook,* pp. 20–24, 29, 30

*See *Materials to Prepare,* p. 95.

Ten-Minute Math

More or Less? Write the problem 56¢ + 61¢ on the board and follow the procedure as described on page 116. If time remains, pose similar problems such as $0.47 + $0.48 + $0.12 and $0.32 + $0.18 + $0.64.

Teaching Note

❶ Explaining the Assessment Because timed work can make some students anxious, talk with them directly about why you want them to solve as many problems as they can in 5 minutes, and how that will help both you and them find out which combinations they still need to work on. If students do seem anxious before the assessment, take time to discuss what could help them figure out which problems they can tackle easily.

Name _____ Date _____

Trading Stickers, Combining Coins

Assessment: Addition Combinations

8 + 5 =	4 + 7 =	3 + 9 =
7 + 9 =	4 + 4 =	6 + 4 =
3 + 6 =	9 + 4 =	7 + 6 =
8 + 10 =	8 + 7 =	5 + 7 =
10 + 9 =	6 + 6 =	9 + 9 =
5 + 6 =	10 + 6 =	6 + 3 =
8 + 9 =	3 + 8 =	5 + 4 =
5 + 8 =	8 + 6 =	9 + 5 =
3 + 7 =	7 + 8 =	10 + 7 =
8 + 4 =	9 + 6 =	7 + 7 =
8 + 8 =	5 + 3 =	9 + 7 =

M44 Unit 1   Session 2.5

▲ Resource Masters, M44

MATH WORKSHOP

❶ Adding to 100 and Story Problems

60 MIN

During this Math Workshop, small groups of students complete a timed assessment while the rest of the students continue practicing addition and subtraction strategies with games and story problems. Take a couple of minutes before Math Workshop begins to explain the structure and purpose of the assessment to the whole class (see discussion below).❶

Advise students to make sure that they all spend time on Activity 1C: Story Problems, since they will discuss this work in the next session.

1A Assessment: Addition Combinations

INDIVIDUALS

Use Assessment: Addition Combinations (M44) to assess students in small groups. Observing the small groups will give you a chance to see which addition combinations up to 10 + 10 students know fluently. This assessment addresses Benchmark 1.

The assessment has 33 addition combinations. +1 and +2 combinations are not included, because it is assumed that third graders know these. Some doubles (3 + 3, 5 + 5, and 10 + 10) are not included for the same reason. A few pairs of the same numbers in reverse order (for example, 8 + 5 and 5 + 8) are included to help you assess whether students recognize that these have the same sum.

The goal is for students to solve these 33 problems accurately in 5 minutes or less. Students need to know that they should work as quickly as they can. Explain that you are trying to help them learn which combinations they know readily and which they are still having trouble with.

This timed assessment will show which problems a student still needs to work on.

Structure this assessment so that you get the information you want, without leaving students frustrated that they are not allowed to finish. One approach is to have students complete as many problems as they can in 5 minutes, skipping around to answer the ones they "just know" first. At the end of 5 minutes, they stop and circle the problems they have not yet solved. Then they continue solving these problems. This gives you a clear record of which problems they needed more time to complete.

After you have had a chance to review students' work on this assessment, decide which addition combinations you will assign to individuals, small groups, or the class as a whole for homework for Session 2.6.

When you know which combinations still need work, use Blank Addition Combinations (M45) to create tailored assessments for ongoing use.

ONGOING ASSESSMENT: Observing Students at Work

Students demonstrate fluency with addition combinations.

- **Are students able to solve addition combinations quickly and accurately?**

- **Are there particular categories of combinations (for example, near-doubles or +9 combinations) with which they need more practice?**

DIFFERENTIATION: Supporting the Range of Learners

Intervention Many students know most of these combinations, but some may need an opportunity either to take the assessment more than once or to continue practicing a few facts that you can assess individually later on.❷ You can also cut apart the assessment so that students have fewer problems to solve at one time.

1B Make a Dollar
PAIRS

For complete details about this activity, see Session 2.4, pages 119–120.

1C Story Problems
INDIVIDUALS

Students solve story problems on *Student Activity Book* page 49. Observe students at work, and make a note of those who are adding by place or adding one number in parts. You will ask some of these students to share their strategies in the discussion that opens the next session.

Professional Development

❷ **Teacher Note:** Assessment: Addition Combinations, p. 161.

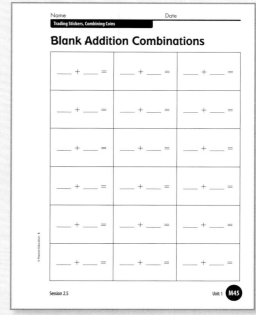

▲ **Resource Masters, M45**

Name _____ Date _____
Trading Stickers, Combining Coins

Story Problems 4
Solve each problem, show your work, and write an equation.

1. 67 third graders and 53 fourth graders went on a field trip to the art museum. How many students went on the field trip in all?

2. Tasha had $2.00. At the store, she bought a notebook that cost 68¢. How much money does she have now?

3. Robby brought bottles and cans to the recycling center. He got $1.25 for the cans and $0.55 for the bottles. How much money did he get in all?

Session 2.5   Unit 1   49

▲ **Student Activity Book, p. 49**

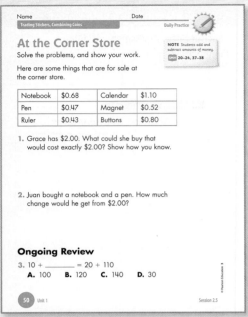

Name _____ Date _____
Trading Stickers, Combining Coins

At the Corner Store
Solve the problems, and show your work.

NOTE Students add and
subtract amounts of money.
20–24, 37–38

Here are some things that are for sale at
the corner store.

Notebook	$0.68	Calendar	$1.10
Pen	$0.47	Magnet	$0.52
Ruler	$0.43	Buttons	$0.80

1. Grace has $2.00. What could she buy that
   would cost exactly $2.00? Show how you know.

2. Juan bought a notebook and a pen. How much
   change would he get from $2.00?

Ongoing Review

3. $10 + \underline{\hspace{1cm}} = 20 + 110$
   A. 100   **B.** 120   **C.** 140   **D.** 30

50   Unit 1   Session 2.5

▲ **Student Activity Book, p. 50**

ONGOING ASSESSMENT: Observing Students at Work

Students solve problems that involve adding and subtracting 2-digit
and 3-digit numbers.

- **Can students write equations that accurately represent the
  problems?** Do they solve the problems accurately?

- **What addition strategies are students using?** Do they add by
  place, combining the tens and ones separately and then adding the
  totals? Do they add on one number in parts? Do they use tools to
  solve these problems?

- **How do students solve the subtraction problems?** Do they use
  their knowledge of subtracting 10 or multiples of 10 to subtract
  the second number in parts? Do they represent the first number
  with cubes or stickers and then "take away" the second number by
  removing or crossing out that number of cubes or stickers?

DIFFERENTIATION: Supporting the Range of Learners

Intervention If students are having difficulty, ask them to model the
action of these problems with cubes or by making sketches of stickers.
Consider changing some of the numbers in the problems so that
students are adding or subtracting smaller amounts.

1D *Close to 100*   **PAIRS**

For complete details about this activity, see Session 2.2, pages 103–108.

SESSION FOLLOW-UP

2 Daily Practice

 Daily Practice: For ongoing review, have students complete
Student Activity Book page 50.

 Student Math Handbook: Students and families may use
Student Math Handbook pages 20–24, 29, 30 for reference and
review. See pages 174–181 in the back of this unit.

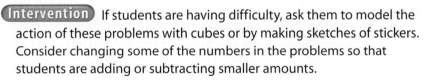

Story Problem Strategies

Math Focus Points

◆ Solving addition problems with 2-digit numbers by using strategies that involve breaking numbers apart by place or adding one number in parts

◆ Finding different combinations of 100s, 10s, and 1s for a number and recognizing their equivalence (i.e., 1 hundred, 3 tens, and 7 ones equals 1 hundred, 2 tens, and 17 ones, or 13 tens and 7 ones.)

Today's Plan		Materials
DISCUSSION ① **Story Problem Strategies**	15 MIN CLASS	• *Student Activity Book,* p. 49 (completed in Session 2.5) • Cubes, in towers of 10

MATH WORKSHOP ② **Combinations of 100s, 10s, and 1s**
 ②A Sheets, Strips, and Singles
 ②B *Make a Dollar*
 ②C *Close to 100*
 ②D *Capture 5*
	45 MIN	②A • *Student Activity Book,* p. 51
		  • Cubes, in towers of 10
		②B • Coin Cards (from Session 2.4); M43*
		②C • M30*
		  • Digit Cards (from Session 2.2)
		②D • M4 (from Session 1.5); Change cards (from Session 1.5); M16*
		  • Overhead colored chips; game pieces

SESSION FOLLOW-UP ③ **Daily Practice and Homework**		• M29* • *Student Activity Book,* pp. 52–53 • *Student Math Handbook,* pp. 7–8, 13–15, 36 • M30*

*See *Materials to Prepare,* p. 95.

Ten-Minute Math

More or Less? Write the problem 31 + 33 + 32 on the board and follow the procedure as described on page 109. Then have students find how far from the exact answer their estimate was.

DISCUSSION

① Story Problem Strategies

15 MIN   CLASS

Math Focus Points for Discussion

◆ Solving addition problems with 2-digit numbers by using strategies that involve breaking numbers apart by place or adding one number in parts

For this discussion of work that students did during Math Workshop in the previous session, direct attention to Problem 1 on *Student Activity Book* page 49: "67 third graders and 53 fourth graders went on a field trip to the art museum. How many students went on the field trip in all?"

What is this problem about? What do you know? What are you trying to find out?

Write the problem both horizontally and vertically on the board:

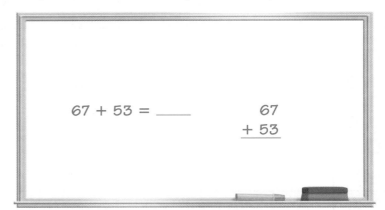

$$67 + 53 = \underline{\hspace{1cm}} \qquad \begin{array}{r} 67 \\ + 53 \\ \hline \end{array}$$

Then ask a student whom you observed adding by place to share his or her strategy.

Students might say:

"First I added 60 plus 50. I know that 50 plus 50 is 100, so this had to be 10 more. That's 110. Then I added the 7 and 3 and got another 10. I added the 110 and 10 together and got 120."

As the student shares, record each step in both equation and vertical notation.

$$67 + 53 = \underline{}$$

$$\begin{array}{r} 67 \\ + 53 \\ \hline \end{array}$$

$$60 + 50 = 110$$

$$\begin{array}{r} 60 \\ + 50 \\ \hline 110 \end{array}$$

110 (60 + 50)
What Zhang
did first

$$7 + 3 = 10$$

$$\begin{array}{r} 7 \\ + 3 \\ \hline 10 \end{array}$$

10 (7 + 3)
What he
did next

$$110 + 10 = 120$$

$$\begin{array}{r} 110 \\ + 10 \\ \hline 120 \end{array}$$

120 (110 + 10)
What he
did last

How can we describe what [Zhang] did to solve this problem? What did he add first? Where did the 60 and 50 come from? What did he do next? Where did he get the 7 and 3?

As students respond, refer to the context of the problem to help students visualize how the steps of the solution relate to the information given. For example:

How many of the third graders has [Zhang] counted so far? How many of the fourth graders? How many more third graders does he need to add in now?

Ask a volunteer to use cubes to show what this student did.

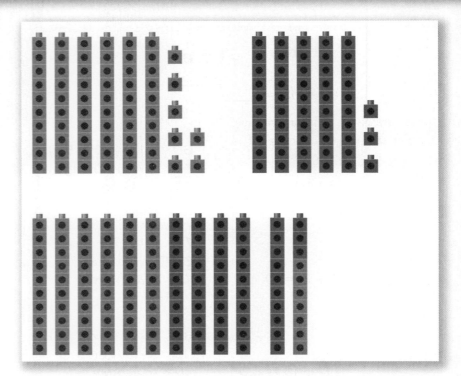

As students share, help them name the strategies.

You noticed that first [Zhang] added the tens, then he added the ones, and then he combined them. Remember, we can call this strategy adding by place.

Next, ask a student to share his or her strategy of adding on one number in parts.

Students might say:

"I started with 67 and added the 3 from the 53. That got me to 70. Then I added 30 from the 50 and got to 100. Then I added the 20 that was left and got 120."

"I started with 67, too, but I added 10s to 77, 87, 97, 107, 117. Then I added the 3 from the 53 to get to 120."

As students share their strategies, record each step in the form of an equation.

Gil

$67 + 3 = 70$

$70 + 30 = 100$

$100 + 20 = 120$

Kim

$67 + 10 = 77$

$77 + 10 = 87$

$87 + 10 = 97$

$97 + 10 = 107$

$107 + 10 = 117$

$117 + 3 = 120$

Then draw an unmarked number line on the board.

I want to show [Gil's] steps on this number line. What number did he start with? [Write 67 on the line.] What did he do next? Where did the 3 come from? How can I show that move on the number line?

We're up to 70. How many of the third graders have we counted so far? (all of them) How many of the fourth graders? (only three)

Continue in this manner until all of the moves are shown on the number line. Then ask a student to represent the second student's strategy on another unmarked number line.

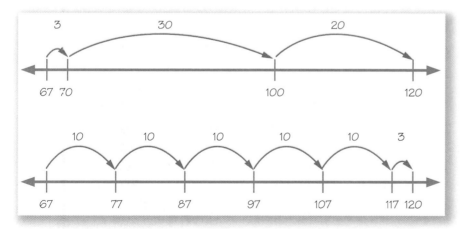

What number did [Kim] start with? What does that number represent in the problem? (third graders) Where did she get the 10 that she added first? What does that number represent? (10 of the 53 fourth graders)

When both number lines are complete, help students relate them to the corresponding sets of equations and compare the two approaches.

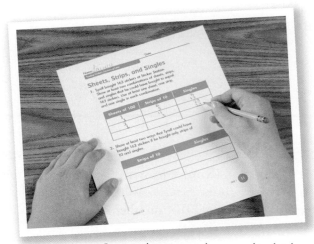

Name _____ Date _____

Trading Stickers, Combining Coins

Sheets, Strips, and Singles

1. Tyrell bought 163 stickers at Sticker Station. Show at least two combinations of sheets, strips, and singles that he could have bought to equal 163 stickers. Use at least one sheet, one strip, and one single in each combination.

Sheets of 100	Strips of 10	Singles

2. Show at least two ways that Tyrell could have bought 163 stickers if he bought only strips of 10 and singles.

Strips of 10	Singles

© Pearson Education 3

Session 2.6   Unit 1   51

▲ **Student Activity Book, p. 51**

What did [Gil] and [Kim] do that is similar? What's different? Where are the 53 fourth graders that they added on? Can you see the 53 on the number line?

Students are likely to comment on the fact that these students both started with 67 and added the 53 in chunks, although they made different decisions about the size of the chunks and the order in which they were added.

So both of these students started with one number in the problem and added the other number in parts. Remember, we can call that strategy *adding one number in parts.*

MATH WORKSHOP

② Combinations of 100s, 10s, and 1s   45 MIN

In this Math Workshop, make sure that all students spend some time on Activity 2A because they will be discussing this work in the next session. You may choose to assign the other activities according to your observations of students' individual needs. Students will continue with the games in Session 2.7 and after the assessment (if time allows) in Session 2.8.

2A Sheets, Strips, and Singles   INDIVIDUALS

Students work on *Student Activity Book* page 51. They find two combinations of sheets, strips, and singles and two combinations of only strips and singles to equal 163 stickers. Let students know that they may look for additional combinations if they choose.

Some students may no longer need to sketch stickers and will record their thinking with numbers.

ONGOING ASSESSMENT: Observing Students at Work

Students find equivalent ways to represent 163 with 100s, 10s, and 1s.

- **Do students' solutions demonstrate knowledge that ten strips of 10 are equivalent to one sheet of 100?** That 1 sheet of 100 and 6 strips of 10 are equal to 16 strips of 10?

- **Are students able to generate multiple combinations of sheets, strips, and singles that total 163?** Do they see connections between different solutions?

DIFFERENTIATION: Supporting the Range of Learners

Intervention Some students might benefit from first representing all the possible combinations for a 2-digit number. Ask those students to begin by representing 63 with strips and singles.

Extension Students moving easily through this activity should be encouraged to find all the possible combinations of stickers for 163. Ask them to think about how they could organize their combinations to prove that they have them all.

2B *Make a Dollar*

PAIRS

For complete details about this activity, see Session 2.4, pages 118–120.

2C *Close to 100*

PAIRS

For complete details about this activity, see Session 2.2, pages 103–108.

2D *Capture 5*

PAIRS

For complete details about this activity, see Session 1.5, pages 61–64.

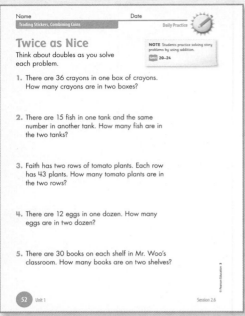

▲ Student Activity Book, p. 52

▲ Student Activity Book, p. 53

SESSION FOLLOW-UP

③ Daily Practice and Homework

 Daily Practice: For ongoing review, have students complete *Student Activity Book* page 52.

Homework: For this assignment, students take home Addition Combinations Practice (M29) with the six combinations you have assigned, according to the results of the assessment in the previous session. Tell students to cut apart the cards at home. On *Student Activity Book* page 53, they record how they worked with a friend or family member on these combinations.

Student Math Handbook: Students and families may use *Student Math Handbook* pages 7–8, 13–15, 36 for reference and review. See pages 174–181 in the back of this unit.

163 Stickers

Math Focus Points

- Finding different combinations of 100s, 10s, and 1s for a number and recognizing their equivalence (i.e., 1 hundred, 3 tens, and 7 ones equals 1 hundred, 2 tens, and 17 ones, or 13 tens and 7 ones)

- Recognizing and demonstrating the equivalence of one 100 to ten 10s and of one 10 to ten 1s

Today's Plan		Materials
DISCUSSION **①** **Sheets, Strips, and Singles**	15 MIN CLASS	• *Student Activity Book,* p. 51 • Cubes, in towers of 10
MATH WORKSHOP **②** **Hundreds, Tens, and Ones** **2A** Hundreds, Tens, and Ones **2B** *Make a Dollar* **2C** *Close to 100* **2D** *Capture 5*	45 MIN	**2A** • *Student Activity Book,* p. 55 • Coin and Dollar Sets; cubes; M12*; M18* **2B** • Coin Cards (from Session 2.4); M43* **2C** • Digit Cards (from Session 2.2); M36* **2D** • M4, Change Cards (from Session 1.5); M16* • Overhead colored chips; game pieces
SESSION FOLLOW-UP **③** **Daily Practice and Homework**		• *Student Activity Book,* pp. 56–57 • *Student Math Handbook,* pp. 7–8, 9 • M29*

*See *Materials to Prepare,* p. 95.

Ten-Minute Math

More or Less? Write the problem $37 + 21 + 56$ on the board and follow the procedure as described on page 109. Then have students find how far from the exact answer their estimate was.

DISCUSSION
Sheets, Strips, and Singles

15 MIN   CLASS

Math Focus Points for Discussion

◆ Finding different combinations of 100s, 10s, and 1s for a number, and recognizing their equivalence (1 hundred, 3 tens, and 7 ones equals 1 hundred, 2 tens, and 17 ones, or 13 tens and 7 ones)

◆ Recognizing and demonstrating the equivalence of one 100 to ten 10s and of one 10 to ten 1s

For this discussion of work that students did during Math Workshop in the previous session, direct attention to *Student Activity Book* page 51 and ask students to share some of the combinations of 100s, 10s, and 1s they found for Tyrell's 163 stickers.

When you have a good list, choose two or three combinations from the list, one using more singles than the other(s). For example:

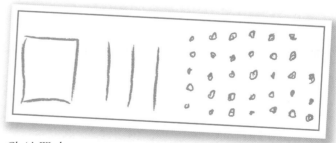

Jung's Work

Chris's Work

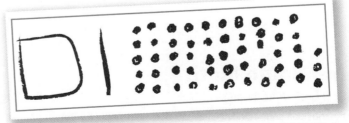

Keith's Work

[Jung's] combination was one sheet of 100, four strips of 10, and 23 singles. What do you notice when you compare [Jung's] and [Chris's] combinations? How are they similar? How are they different? How many more singles are in [Chris's] combination? Where did the extra singles come from?

[Keith] used only 1 strip of 10. How many singles were in his combination? Where are all those singles represented in Jung's combination?

After comparing several combinations, ask students about the meaning of the digits in the number 163.

Let's look at the number 163. [Write 163 on the board.] What does the 1 in this number tell you? What about the 6? The 3? What if you look at the 6 and 3 together? [Underline the 6 and 3.] What does the 63 in 163 tell you? Did anyone use 1 sheet of 100 and 63 singles to make this number?

Ask students to share some of the combinations of 163 stickers they found that contained only strips of 10 and singles. List these as well. Then ask questions such as the following:

If you don't use a sheet of 100, what is the greatest number of strips of 10 you can use to make 163 stickers? Why can't you use more than 16 strips of 10? What happens to the singles every time you use one less strip of 10? How many singles do you have if you use only 13 strips of 10? 10 strips of 10?

Underline the hundred and tens digits together:

16̲3

Now look at these two digits together. What does the 16 in this number tell you?

This question can be a difficult one for third graders. Spend a few minutes discussing it. Some students will understand that these digits represent the maximum number of 10s that compose the 3-digit number. Ask students whether they can show with a sticker sketch how the digits 16 in 163 represent 16 tens.

Some of you are saying that the 16 in 163 tells you that there are 16 tens in that number. Can we tell the number of 10s by the first two digits in *any* 3-digit number? How about 137? What does the 13 tell you in that number? What about 185? What does the 18 tell you in that number? How do you know?

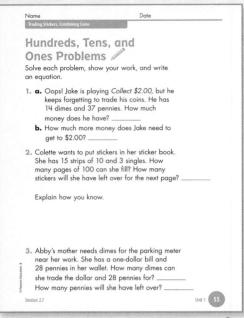

▲ **Student Activity Book, p. 55**

Students will continue to work on determining the number of 10s in 3-digit numbers in the Grade 3 unit, *How Many Hundreds? How Many Miles.*

MATH WORKSHOP

② Hundreds, Tens, and Ones

45 MIN

In this Math Workshop, all students should spend time on Activity 2A. The remaining activities offer further practice through familiar games. You might assign these according to your observations of students' individual needs. Students may continue with these Math Workshop activities after they have finished the End-of-Unit Assessment in Session 2.8.

2A Hundreds, Tens, and Ones

INDIVIDUALS

Students work on problems on *Student Activity Book* page 55 that focus on equivalencies of 100s, 10s, and 1s.

ONGOING ASSESSMENT: Observing Students at Work

Students solve problems involving relationships among hundreds, tens, and ones in the contexts of money and stickers.

- **Do students use tools such as cubes, coins, or 100 grids to solve the problems, or are they able to solve them by reasoning about the numbers?**

- **Do their solutions demonstrate understanding of the equivalence of ten pennies to one dime/10 ones to 1 ten and ten dimes to one dollar/10 tens to 1 hundred?**

- **What tools and/or strategies do students use to determine the difference between $1.77 and $2.00 in Problem 1?** Do they use number lines or a 200 chart? Do they use known combinations that add to 100 or a dollar to help them?

DIFFERENTIATION: Supporting the Range of Learners

Intervention Some students may still use coins or cubes to represent the numbers in each problem. In Problem 1, for example, students may take 14 dimes and 37 pennies from their coin collections. These students may still be counting by 10s and 1s to determine the total amount of money before trading for larger coins or bills. Help them think about how to use equivalencies by asking questions such as these:

I see that you have 14 dimes. Can you trade any of those dimes for one dollar? How many dimes would that be? How many dimes are left? You have 37 pennies. Can you trade some of them for dimes? How many pennies will you have left?

Help students think about using what they know about combinations that make 100 to solve larger problems.

What if you had $0.77? How much more would you need to make a dollar? Can you show me how you can use a number line (or a 100 or 200 chart) to figure it out? If you know that $0.77 plus $0.23 equals a dollar, how can that help you figure out how much to add to $1.77 to make $2.00?

Help students use math tools such as the 200 chart to work out the problems.

2B Make a Dollar

PAIRS

For complete details about this activity, see Session 2.4, pages 118–120.

▲ Student Activity Book, p. 56

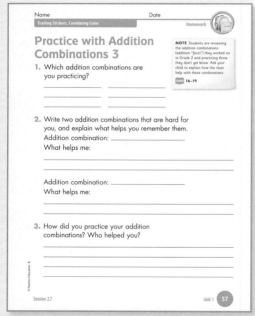

▲ Student Activity Book, p. 57

2C Close to 100

PAIRS

For complete details about this activity, see Session 2.2, pages 103–108.

2D Capture 5

PAIRS

For complete details about this activity, see Session 1.5, pages 61–64.

SESSION FOLLOW-UP

3 Daily Practice and Homework

Daily Practice: For ongoing review, have students complete *Student Activity Book* page 56.

Homework: Supply a copy of Addition Combinations Practice (M29) to each student. Students choose six combinations, fill in the cards, and cut apart the cards for practice at home with a friend or family member. They record their notes about this practice on *Student Activity Book* page 57.

Student Math Handbook: Students and families may use *Student Math Handbook* pages 7–8, 9 for reference and review. See pages 174–181 in the back of this unit.

End-of-Unit Assessment

Math Focus Points

◆ Adding and subtracting multiples of 10

◆ Solving addition problems with 2-digit numbers by using strategies that involve breaking numbers apart by place or adding one number in parts

◆ Finding different combinations of 100s, 10s, and 1s for a number and recognizing their equivalence (i.e., 1 hundred, 3 tens, and 7 ones equals 1 hundred, 2 tens, and 17 ones, or 13 tens and 7 ones)

Today's Plan	Materials
ASSESSMENT ACTIVITY **①** **End-of-Unit Assessment** ✔ 🕐 🧍 **60 MIN INDIVIDUALS**	• M46–M48*
SESSION FOLLOW-UP **②** **Daily Practice**	• *Student Activity Book*, p. 59 • *Student Math Handbook*, pp. 7–8, 20–24, 36

*See *Materials to Prepare*, p. 95.

Ten-Minute Math

More or Less? Write the problem $67 + 12 + 23$ on the board. Students estimate the sum and decide if it is more or less than 100. Select students to share their strategies.

What did you pay attention to when you looked at these numbers?

Did you use combinations you know that equal 100 or $1.00 to help you?

How far from the exact answer was your estimate?

If some students mentally calculated the exact answer, ask them to share the answer and their strategy with the class. If time remains, pose similar problems such as $33 + 45 + 21$.

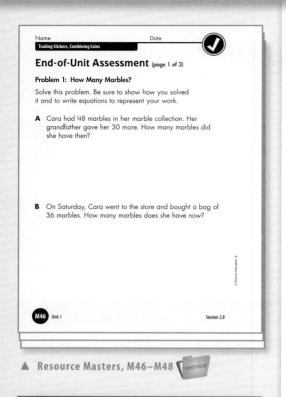

Name _____ Date _____

Trading Stickers, Combining Coins

End-of-Unit Assessment (page 1 of 3)

Problem 1: How Many Marbles?

Solve this problem. Be sure to show how you solved it and to write equations to represent your work.

A Cara had 48 marbles in her marble collection. Her grandfather gave her 30 more. How many marbles did she have then?

B On Saturday, Cara went to the store and bought a bag of 36 marbles. How many marbles does she have now?

M46 Unit 1   Session 2.8

▲ **Resource Masters, M46–M48** PORTFOLIO

Professional Development

❶ **Teacher Note:** End-of-Unit Assessment, p. 164

ASSESSMENT ACTIVITY

❶ End-of-Unit Assessment

60 MIN INDIVIDUALS

This End-of-Unit Assessment focuses on three of the unit's benchmarks. ❶

Provide students with copies of the End-of-Unit Assessment (M46–M48). Students work individually to solve three assessment problems.

Problem 1 assesses Benchmark 3: Solve problems with 2-digit addends and addresses Benchmark 4: Break up 3-digit numbers (less than 200) into 100s, 10s, and 1s in different ways. Problem 2 assesses students' use of known combinations and knowledge of place value to find pairs of numbers that equal 100. This problem addresses Benchmark 5: Find combinations of 2-digit numbers that add to 100 or $1.00. Problem 3 assesses students' ability to break up numbers into 100s, 10s, and 1s in different ways. It addresses Benchmark 4.

ONGOING ASSESSMENT: Observing Students at Work

Students use their knowledge of addition, subtraction, and the number system to solve the problems on the assessment.

- **How do students add a multiple of 10 to a 2-digit number?** Are they able to add the multiple in one step, or do they break it into 10s and add one 10 at a time?

- **What addition strategies do students use?** Do they add each place and then combine the sums? Do they add on one number in parts? Do they do this efficiently, adding multiples of 10s and 1s? What representations do students use to solve the problem and record their strategy?

- **Are students able to find pairs of 2-digit numbers that add to 100?** What strategies do they use to do so?

- **Are students able to represent a 3-digit number with different combinations of 100, 10s, and 1s?** Can they represent the same number with different combinations of tens and ones?

DIFFERENTIATION: Supporting the Range of Learners

Intervention If some students can solve the problems but are having trouble writing down their strategies, have them explain their thinking to you and record it on their paper. Note that these students may need ongoing support in recording their strategies for themselves.

SESSION FOLLOW-UP

2 Daily Practice

 Daily Practice: For enrichment, have students complete *Student Activity Book* page 59. This page provides real-world problems involving the math content of this unit.

 Student Math Handbook: Students and families may use *Student Math Handbook* pages 7–8, 20–24, 36 for reference and review. See pages 174–181 in the back of this unit.

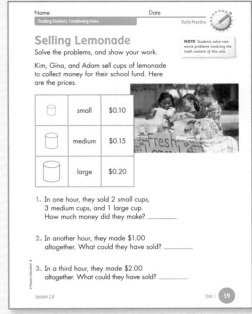

Name _____ Date _____
Trading Stickers, Combining Coins   Daily Practice

Selling Lemonade

NOTE Students solve real-world problems involving the math content of this unit.

Solve the problems, and show your work.

Kim, Gina, and Adam sell cups of lemonade to collect money for their school fund. Here are the prices.

	small	$0.10
	medium	$0.15
	large	$0.20

1. In one hour, they sold 2 small cups, 3 medium cups, and 1 large cup. How much money did they make? _____

2. In another hour, they made $1.00 altogether. What could they have sold? _____

3. In a third hour, they made $2.00 altogether. What could they have sold? _____

Session 2.8   Unit 1 59

▲ **Student Activity Book, p. 59**

Professional Development

UNIT 1

Trading Stickers, Combining Coins

Teacher Notes

In Part 6 of *Implementing Investigations in Grade 3,* you will find a set of Teacher Notes that addresses topics and issues applicable to the curriculum as a whole rather than to specific curriculum units. They include the following:

Computational Fluency and Place Value

Computational Algorithms and Methods

Representations and Contexts for Mathematical Work

Foundations of Algebra in the Elementary Grades

Discussing Mathematical Ideas

Racial and Linguistic Diversity in the Classroom:
   What Does Equity Mean in Today's Math Classroom?

Dialogue Boxes

Place Value

In Grade 3, students solidify their understanding of the base-ten number system as they learn to use and understand numbers in the 100s and 1,000s. The base-ten number system is a "place value" system; that is, any numeral can represent different values, depending on where it appears in a written number: the numeral 2 can represent 2 ones, 2 tens, 2 hundreds, 2 thousands, and so forth. Understanding our place value system requires coordinating the way we write the numerals that represent a particular number (e.g., 217) and the way we name numbers in words (e.g., two hundred seventeen), with how those symbols represent quantities. See **Part 6: Professional Development** in *Implementing Investigations in Grade 3:* Computational Fluency and Place Value.

The Base-Ten Number System

In Grade 3, students first focus on how 100 is composed in this unit, *Trading Stickers, Combining Coins*. Later, they look at how multiples of 100, including numbers in the 1,000s, are composed in the unit *Collections and Travel Stories*. The heart of this work is learning to relate the written numerals to a quantity and to how that quantity is composed. This is not simply a matter of saying that 217 "has 2 hundreds, 1 ten, and 7 ones," which students can easily learn to do without attaching meaning to the quantity these numerals represent. Students must learn to visualize how 217 is built up from hundreds, tens, and ones in a way that helps them relate its value to other quantities. That is, understanding the place value of 217 entails knowing that 217 is closer to 200 than to 300, that it is 100 more than 117, that it is 17 more than 200, that it is 3 less than 220, and that it is composed of 21 tens and 7 ones.

In this unit, students use two contexts—stickers and money—to build 3-digit numbers and visualize how they are composed. They focus on creating different combinations of stickers or coins to make a certain quantity. For example, 117 can be composed of 1 sheet of 100, 1 strip of 10, and 7 individual stickers (or 1 dollar, 1 dime, and 7 pennies), but it can also be composed of 11 strips of 10 and 7 individual stickers (or 11 dimes and 7 pennies). Students work on visualizing the composition of these numbers flexibly.

Place Value and Computational Fluency

A thorough understanding of the base-ten number system is one of the critical building blocks for developing computational fluency. The composition of numbers from multiples of 1, 10, 100, 1,000, and so on, is the basis of most of the strategies students use for computation with whole numbers.

Throughout their work in Grade 3, students learn about using multiples of 10 and 100 as "landmarks" in their computation work. In this unit, students focus on adding and subtracting multiples of 10 (for example, in the game *Capture 5,* introduced in Investigation 1) and on combinations that add to 100 (for example, in the Ten-Minute Math activity, *More or Less,* introduced in Investigation 2).

By considering which digits of a number will change when multiples of 1, 10, or 100 are added or subtracted, students focus on a key aspect of estimation—looking carefully at the place value of the numbers in a problem. For example, consider these two problems:

$$32 + 30 = \underline{\hspace{2cm}}$$

$$32 + 3 = \underline{\hspace{2cm}}$$

Sample Student Work

How does the sum compare with 32 in each case? Students think about how the first sum will now have 6 tens, but the ones will not change, whereas in the second sum, the ones will change, but the tens remain the same. Considering the magnitude of the numbers in addition and subtraction problems leads to a reasonable estimate of the result. The work with tens and ones in this unit lays the foundation for estimation with larger numbers later in Grade 3.

The single-digit addition combinations (the "facts") are critical for computational fluency in addition, but so are other addition combinations. In this unit, students should develop a solid grasp of the 2-digit combinations that make the sum of 100, as they picture how 100 can be decomposed into tens and ones. For example, consider the following equation:

Sample Student Work

Through visualizing 38 in the sticker context or by thinking about money, students come to recognize easily that 38 + 2 = 40, and 40 + 60 = 100, so 38 + 62 = 100.

In this case, 38 is composed of 3 tens and part of another ten. In order to complete the addition expression so that the sum is 100, or ten 10s, students think, "Two more ones will give me 4 tens, then I need 6 more tens (60) to get to 100, so that's 62 altogether." Students can use coins or sticker sketches to help them visualize this relationship, but eventually they should be able to do any problem of this sort mentally. When students can easily compute any missing addend to make the sum of 100, they can use this information to find the sums of related problems, such as 38 + _____ = 200. They begin this work with multiples of 100 in this unit and continue it in *Collections and Travel Stories.*

Students' work on adding and subtracting relates directly to their work on the place value system. The two strategies for addition emphasized in this unit—*adding by place* and *adding on one number in parts*—depend on an understanding of how to decompose numbers.

The focus for students in this unit is on understanding the structure of 100 and using that understanding to solve addition and subtraction problems. Students need to spend plenty of time working with 100 in a variety of contexts and activities in order to develop the foundation for computational fluency. In *Collections and Travel Stories,* students will work with multiples of 100 and numbers in the 1,000s.

Stickers: A Context for Place Value

In Grade 2, students made a critical shift from thinking and working primarily in ones, to thinking and working with groups of ones and tens. Students were introduced to a context particularly focused on groups of 10—a store that sells stickers individually (singles or ones) or in strips of 10. They worked to determine the total number of stickers when given some number of strips and singles. Also, when given a number, they figured out how to show that amount with strips and singles. Through these activities, most students came to understand that ten 1s is equivalent to one group of 10.

Later in Grade 2, students worked on addition and subtraction story problems within the context of stickers. This work helped students develop more efficient strategies for solving addition and subtraction problems. For example, as students became more comfortable with the idea of *one 10,* they were less likely to count all or count on by 1s.

Instead, when solving a problem like 33 + 24, the sticker context encouraged them to add tens and ones (e.g., 30 + 20 = 50, 3 + 4 = 7, 50 + 7 = 57) or to add on one number in parts (e.g., 33 + 10 + 10 = 53, 53 + 4 = 57).

In Grade 2, students were also introduced to sheets of 100 stickers, organized in rows of 10. These sheets extended their thinking about place value—how numbers in our number system are structured (in ones, tens, hundreds, etc). It also helped students achieve a strong understanding of how 100 is composed.

This Grade 3 unit, *Trading Stickers, Combining Coins,* extends the sticker context as students work with sheets of 100 in addition to strips of 10 and singles.

In this unit, students determine the total number of stickers when given some number of sheets, strips, and singles (e.g., "How many stickers are 2 sheets of 100, 5 strips of 10, and 7 singles?") They also represent 2- and 3-digit numbers with stickers (e.g., "Show the number 157 with stickers"). Students come to see the equivalence of different combinations of 100s, 10s, and 1s for the same number. For example, the number 137 can be composed from 1 hundred, 3 tens, and 7 ones; 1 hundred and 37 ones; 13 tens and 7 ones; or 12 tens and 17 ones, and so on.

Encourage students to use a shorthand notation to show hundreds, tens, and ones so that they do not spend time drawing each individual sticker. They can sketch squares to represent hundreds; lines to represent strips of ten; and dots or circles to represent ones, or "singles." For example, a simple sketch of 257 could look like this:

Sample Student Work

You can also use this shorthand notation yourself whenever you sketch a combination of stickers. (Throughout this unit, the singles are conventionally grouped in lines of five because it often helps students visualize the numbers.)

Students also continue and extend work from Grade 2 on adding and subtracting 10s. They do this by using the sticker context to examine what happens when multiples of 10 and 100 are added to or subtracted from 2- and 3-digit numbers. They solve sticker story problems in which they add 2-digit numbers with sums over 100. As in previous grades, these problems encourage students to add by place or to add on one number in parts.

In *"How many more?"* problems, students determine how many more stickers they need to equal one or more sheets of 100. For example: Isaac has 43 stickers. How many more stickers does he need to have 100 stickers in all? Angela has 136 stickers. How many more does she need to have 200 stickers?

Later in Grade 3, students extend their understanding of place value as they examine the structure of 1,000. In Grades 4 and 5, students will investigate the structure of much larger numbers (thousands, ten thousands, and hundred thousands).

Mathematical Representations for Addition and Subtraction

As students work on addition and subtraction, it is important for them to develop visual images to help them make sense of problems, solve them, and represent the strategies they use. Students may develop their own images as they work on addition and subtraction. However, throughout the *Investigations* curriculum, they are also introduced to specific representations that they are encouraged to use as they solve problems.

In earlier grades, students used a variety of manipulatives and representations to make sense of numbers and operations. In this unit, use of the following math tools and representations is continued from earlier grades:

- interlocking cubes (stored in towers of 10 for ease of use and counting out how many are needed, and to reinforce the concept of 10 as the basis of our number system)

- 100 chart

- 200 chart (introduced in this unit)

- sets of coins and dollars

- class number line

- place value model: stickers as "singles" (units) and "strips" (tens)

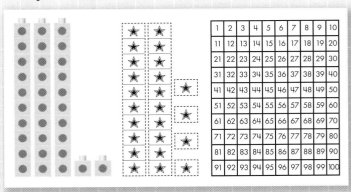

Two of these models are extended in this unit: the place value model and the number line.

The Place Value Model

In Grade 3, the place value model with stickers is extended to include sheets of 100, which are shown as 10×10 arrays. This place value model highlights the structure of numbers in our base 10 number system. See *Implementing Investigations in Grade 3* for more about students' work with place value in this curriculum. The **Teacher Note: Stickers: A Context for Place Value**, page 145, explains how the sticker context supports this work. Students also use 100 grids (and sometimes strips of 10s and singles) as a representation for addition and subtraction in problems outside the sticker context.

As students solve addition and subtraction problems, they use this model to consider what happens when multiples of 10 are added to or subtracted from numbers. They also use this model to break numbers apart by place as they solve multidigit addition and subtraction problems. Students also use a 100 grid to visualize how a 2-digit number relates to 100, an important landmark in our number system. Later in Grade 3, they use this model to construct 1,000 and visualize how 2- and 3-digit numbers relate to 1,000.

The Number Line

In Grades K–4, a number line that extends from −20 to 120 is displayed in the classroom. Students also learn how to represent their strategies on an unmarked number line, showing only those numbers that are relevant to the problem. As students add or subtract quantities in groups or chunks as well as by ones, they mark these moves with curved lines and arrows or "jumps" on the number line. For example, for the problem 78 + _____ = 100, one student showed her work as follows:

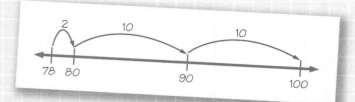

Number lines help students better understand how a quantity increases or decreases, as some amount is added to or subtracted from it. When adding two numbers, students can visualize starting at the number that represents the first addend and adding the second addend by taking one or several jumps on the number line (see Figure A).

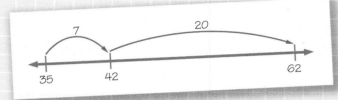

Figure A. 35 + 27 = 62

They can visualize a subtraction problem either as the distance between the two numbers, or as a jump back on the number line. In the first case, the difference is represented by the jumps taken (see Figure B), so the answer is the distance between the two numbers on the number line. In the second case, the difference is represented by the number where the jumps end (see Figure C), and the jumps backward represent the amount being subtracted.

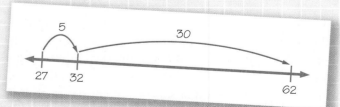

Figure B. 62 −27 = 35 (distance on the line)

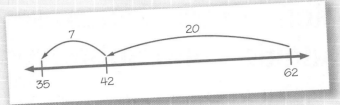

Figure C. 62 − 27 = 35 (where jumps end)

Using a Variety of Models and Tools

Place value models and number lines help students to develop images about what is happening in problems, and to think about ways to solve them. They also highlight important aspects of our number system and number relationships. Therefore, using these representations helps students develop efficient problem-solving strategies based on their understanding of our number system.

In Grade 3, students expand their knowledge of math tools for whole-number computation. When asked to represent their thinking about an idea they are exploring, they can choose whichever math tool best captures how they are visualizing the number relationships and the action of the problem. Consequently, a variety of math tools and representations should be available at all times for students to use when they need to explain, verify, or further explore their thinking.

Students can be expected to use math tools both to solve problems and to represent their thinking. After students have become comfortable with a math tool or representation, they can begin to use it for mental reference. For example, when a student needs help solving a problem, you might say, "Imagine what this problem would look like on a number line—what do you see?" Over time, students internalize these tools and representations.

Addition Strategies

Students' strategies for addition fall into two basic categories: (1) breaking the numbers apart and then adding these parts; and (2) changing the numbers to numbers that are easier to add. Early in Grade 3, most students will be using strategies in the first category, which are described in more detail below. They will investigate the second category later this year. The second category strategies are described briefly here, in case you have some students who are already using this approach.

To develop good addition strategies, students must understand the meaning of addition and have a sound mental model of what is happening in the problem. They must be able to look at the problem as a whole, think about the relationships of the numbers in the problem, and choose an approach that they can carry out easily and accurately.

By the end of this unit, third-grade students should be able to break apart 2-digit numbers in a variety of ways, add the parts accurately, keep track of all the parts of a problem, and combine the parts to find the sum of the original problem. They should feel comfortable and confident with at least one strategy, and be using it efficiently—adding the largest or most reasonable parts of the number and using a small number of steps.

Following are examples of students' strategies, with all the steps for each strategy written out in detail. In practice, however, students gradually learn to carry out many of these steps mentally, jotting down just what they need to keep track of partial sums.

Breaking the Numbers Apart

In strategies that involve breaking numbers apart and then adding the parts, students use their understanding of the ways in which numbers can be decomposed. Strategies generally fall into two types: *adding by place* and *adding on one number in parts*.

Set A: Adding by place In these solutions, students break the numbers apart by place value, add each place, and then find a final total. Students might call these approaches "adding by place" or "adding hundreds, tens, and ones."

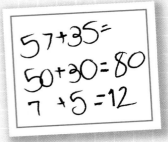
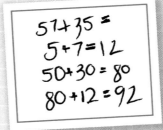

Sample Student Work   *Sample Student Work*

The first student added by place, starting with the largest place. The second student started by adding the ones.

Students should also become familiar with vertical notation for this method.

$$
\begin{array}{ll}
57 & \qquad 57 \\
+35 & \qquad +35 \\
\hline
80\ (50 + 30) & \qquad 12\ (7 + 5) \\
\underline{12}\ (7 + 5) & \qquad \underline{80}\ (50 + 30) \\
92\ (80 + 12) & \qquad 92\ (12 + 80)
\end{array}
$$

The parenthetical expressions next to each partial sum indicate which parts of the numbers are added. Recording these expressions helps students understand what is happening, but they are not expected to include these expressions in their own notation.

Place value models—such as 100 grids, or stickers that come in sheets of 100, strips of 10, and singles—help students visualize what is happening when they break apart numbers by place and then add. For example, a student might describe part of the problem 57 + 35 this way:

"When I had to add 50 plus 30, I thought of it as 5 strips of (10) stickers and 3 strips. Five strips and three strips make 8 strips, and 8 strips is 80 stickers."

The U.S. "carrying" algorithm, which some third grade students may be familiar with, is also an example of adding by place. Rather than beginning with the largest place, as students often do naturally, this algorithm begins with the smallest place. It includes a shorthand way of notating the value of the numbers as the digits in each place are added. For many third graders, the compressed notation of this algorithm can obscure both the place value of the numbers and the meaning of each step of the procedure. This can lead to a more rote approach to solving addition problems, while students are still solidifying their understanding of the base-ten number system and the operation of addition in Grade 3—steps in students' development of computational fluency that take time and practice.

After students have developed good, efficient algorithms that they understand and can carry out easily, such as

adding by place, some may also become fluent in the traditional or standard algorithm. Others will continue to use adding by place or adding on in parts fluently, which will also serve them well for their computation needs now and as adults. The U.S. "carrying" algorithm is not addressed directly in Grade 3, although some students may be able to use it with understanding. Note that the vertical notation of adding by place shown on the previous page, in which the ones are added first, is closely related to the steps in the standard algorithm but makes these steps more transparent. When students use the standard algorithm, demonstrate this form of notation and help students compare the two. Students who use the standard algorithm should also learn other strategies that demonstrate their flexibility with and understanding of addition. The U.S. algorithm is included in a study of strategies for addition in Grade 4.

Set B: Adding one number in parts Some students break up one of the addends into parts and then add these parts, one at a time, to the other number.

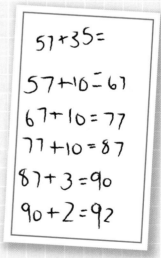

Sample Student Work

57+35=

57+30=87

87+3=90

90+2=92

Sample Student Work

51+35=

57+3=60

60+32=92

Sample Student Work

Each of these students started with 57, but broke up 35 in different ways: 10 + 10 + 10 + 3 + 2; or 30 + 3 + 2; or 3 + 32. When students use this strategy, they should be encouraged to add the largest "chunks" of numbers they can, while still making sense of the problem and the numbers. Students often use a number line to represent their thinking when using this strategy. Here is how the students' strategies on the previous page might be represented on number lines.

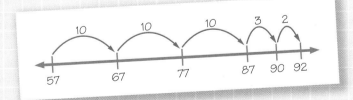

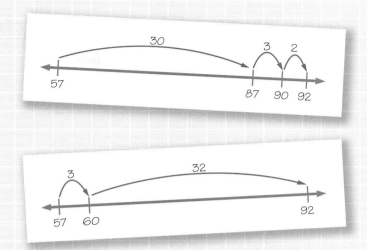

Changing the Numbers

In this category of approaches to solving addition problems, students change one or both of the numbers to what they often call "landmark" or "friendly" numbers—generally multiples of 10 or 100. These strategies require that students understand what they need to do to compensate for the changes they make. For example, a student might think of 57 + 35 as 60 + 35, find the sum of 95, and then subtract 3 from that sum because 3 was added to 57 to get 60. Other students might first solve 57 + 33 because they recognize that this combination results in a sum that is a multiple of 10 and then add on 2. A student might change both numbers, adding to one and subtracting from the other, to create an equivalent problem that is easier to solve.

57+35=60+32=92

Sample Student Work

More detail about this category of strategies is found in the Grade 3 units *Collections and Travel Stories* and *How Many Hundreds? How Many Miles?*.

Does Order Matter in Addition?

In third grade, the question of order in addition can come up for students in a variety of situations.

- When representing addition problems with stickers and strips: "26 + 52 and 52 + 26 are both 7 strips and 8 singles."

- When working on the activity *How Many More Stickers to Get 100?* "If I start with 48, I need 52. If I start with 52, I need 48."

- When adding more than 2 numbers, for example, 34 + 23 + 16: "I did it this way: 34 + 16 is 50, and 50 + 23 = 73."

Many students already realize that when the order of the addends in an addition problem changes, the sum does not. They may explain that this happens because you are just changing the placement of the numbers, but "you are not adding any more or taking anything away."

From a formal mathematical perspective, the ideas these students are working on involve two basic laws of arithmetic. The first is the *commutative law of addition,* which states that two numbers added in either order yield the same sum. Some students call these "opposites," or "switch-arounds," or "reversibles." The very fact that students have given names to this phenomenon indicates that they have formulated a generalization: If you take two numbers and switch them around, you still get the same sum when you add them. Written algebraically, this law can be expressed as $a + b = b + a$.

The second basic law, the *associative law of addition,* states that when three numbers are added together, they can be regrouped without changing the order and will yield the same sum. For example, $(35 + 14) + 6 = 35 + (14 + 6)$. In the expression to the left, first add 35 + 14 to get 49, and then

add 49 + 6. In the expression to the right, first add 14 + 6 to get 20, and then add 35 + 20. (Using parentheses indicates that the operation within the parentheses is to be carried out first.) The sum for both is 55. Written algebraically, this law can be expressed as $(a + b) + c = a + (b + c)$. One calculation is easier than the other; the associative property guarantees that the sum is constant.

When performing addition with two numbers, the commutative law applies. When adding three or more numbers, the reordering might involve the commutative law, the associative law, or both in combination. It is not important for students to learn the formal names of these properties. Rather, they should be encouraged to examine questions about order, and to support their reasoning with various ways to represent addition—such as combining stickers and strips, story contexts, drawings of the situations, number lines, or 100 charts.

As students continue to learn about operations and calculations, questions about order will repeatedly arise: Does order matter when you subtract? What about when you multiply? What about when you divide? (They will find that it does matter when subtracting or dividing but not when adding or multiplying.) Does it matter when you add fractions or integers (which include numbers below zero)? Answering these questions is work ahead of your students in the months and years to come.

Teacher Note

Assessment: Hundreds, Tens, and Ones

Problem 1: How Many More? Part A

Benchmark addressed:

Benchmark 3: Solve addition problems with 2-digit numbers using strategies that involve breaking numbers apart by place or adding one number in parts

In order to meet the benchmark, students' work should show that they can:

- Accurately combine two quantities by breaking the numbers apart by place or by adding on one number in parts;

- Show how they solved the problem;

- Include an equation that matches the situation.

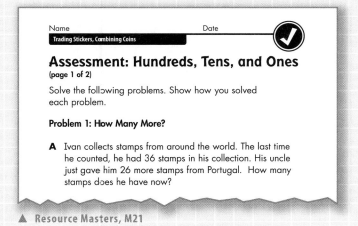

▲ Resource Masters, M21

Meeting the Benchmark

The following examples of student work provide typical responses. All of these students met the benchmark—they were able to interpret the problem, solve it accurately, show their work, and write an equation.

Adding by Place

In these examples, students solve this problem by breaking the 36 and 26 into 10s and 1s. They break 36 into $30 + 6$ and 26 into $20 + 6$, and then combine $30 + 20$. Most students then combine $6 + 6$ and add on 12, either in one step (Elena) or in chunks (Keith).

Elena's Work

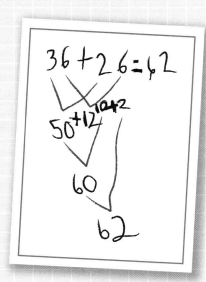

Keith's Work

Adding One Number in Parts

In these examples, students solve this problem by starting with 36 and adding 26 in parts. Pilar added 36 + 20 and then added on 6 in one step. Other variations of this strategy are starting with 36 and adding 10, then 10 more, and then 4 and 2 (36 + 10 = 46, 46 + 10 = 56, 56 + 4 = 60, 60 + 2 = 62), or starting with 26 and adding 36 in parts.

> I know that 36 +20 = 56. So then you add the six more that are left. So then you would get 36 +20 +6 = 62. That is how I got my answer.
> 36 +26 =

Pilar's Work

Partially Meeting the Benchmark

Some students understand the structure of the problem—that it is about combining two groups and finding the total—but make errors as they add or attempt to keep track of the quantities in the problem. For example, a student might correctly break up both numbers into tens and ones but leave out one of the parts when adding them back together. After you review their work, ask these students to look for and correct such errors on their own. Encourage them to take their time and work carefully to avoid similar errors in the future. In addition, note whether these kinds of errors are consistent across problems. If they are, what is causing the difficulty? Is the student losing track of the parts of the numbers? Does the student know how to add multiples of 10? Does the student know the basic addition combinations? Note that students will be reviewing their addition combinations ("facts") in Investigation 2.

Other students understand the structure of the problem and how to solve it but struggle with how to adequately show their work. Ask these students to tell you how they solved the problem in order to probe their understanding. Then, encourage them to add to their written explanation as appropriate. Note that they need more support in finding ways to show their work.

Not Meeting the Benchmark

Students who solve the problem by counting all, like Arthur does, do not meet the benchmark. By Grade 3, students should be adding more efficiently. These students interpret the situation successfully, recognizing that the problem requires combining two amounts. However, they need support in thinking about the composition of the numbers in the problem and how this can help them break the numbers into parts that are easier to add. Ask these students to represent the numbers with place value materials (cubes or stickers) and to show you what happens when they combine the 10s and 1s from each number or when they add tens first and then ones to one of the numbers.

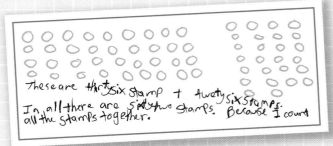

> These are thirty six stamp + twenty six stamps. In all there are fifty two stamps. Because I count all the stamps together.

Arthur's Work

Problem 1: How Many More? Part B

Benchmark addressed (assessed at the end of the unit):

Benchmark 5: Find combinations of 2-digit numbers that equal 100 or $1.00

In order to meet the benchmark, students' work should show that they can:

- Accurately find the difference between a 2-digit number and 100 by adding on from the 2-digit number or beginning at 100 and subtracting;

- Show how they solved the problem.

B Ivan's goal is to collect 100 stamps. How many more stamps does he need?

Session 1.9   Unit 1 **M21**

© Pearson Education 3

▲ **Resource Masters, M21**

Meeting the Benchmark

Some students use models such as number lines or 100 grids to solve this problem and/or to represent their strategies. Gina, for example, used an unmarked number line, started with 62, and jumped by 10s to 72, 82, and 92 and then by 8 to 100. She then combined the jumps to determine that 38 stamps are needed to get to 100.

Gina's Work

Kathryn used an unmarked number line as well, but she started at 100, jumped back 30 to get to 70, and back 8 to get to 62. She too combined her moves to get 38.

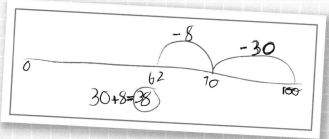

Kathryn's Work

Other students solve the problem numerically, beginning at 62 and adding up to 100, and then combining the parts added ($62 + 8 = 70$, $70 + 30 = 100$, $8 + 30 = 38$). Kenji used a variation of this strategy, adding 8 to the 2 from 62 to make a 10, adding 10 to the 60 to get 70, and then 30 more to get to 100. He was able to keep track of what each number means—that 8 and 30 were the two quantities added on to 62.

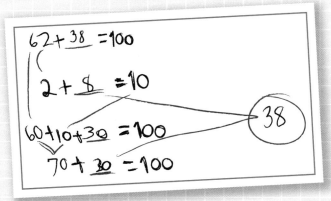

Kenji's Work

Be aware that students who made computation errors in the first part of this problem may successfully find the difference between that incorrect sum and 100. For example, one student incorrectly computed the total number of stamps as 61, but then correctly determined that 39 more were needed to get to 100. This student meets expectations for Problem 1, Part B.

Partially Meeting the Benchmark

Some students understand the structure of the problem—that it is about finding the difference between a 2-digit number and 100—but make errors as they add on to the 2-digit number or subtract back from 100. After you have reviewed their work, ask these students to look for and correct such errors on their own. Encourage them to take their time and work carefully to avoid similar errors in the future. In addition, note whether these kinds of errors are consistent across problems. Does the student lose track of the parts of the problem? Does the student have difficulty adding on or subtracting multiples of 10?

Other students understand the structure of the problem and how to solve it but struggle with showing their work adequately. Ask these students to tell you how they solved the problem, to probe their understanding. Then encourage them to add to their written explanation as appropriate. Note that they need more support in finding ways to show their work.

Not Meeting the Benchmark

Students who determine the number of stamps needed by counting on by ones do not meet the expectations for this part of the assessment. Bridget, for example, has drawn the numbers 63 through 100 and appears to have counted each space. It also appears that she has drawn something like a 100 chart, but does not have a sense of how it is arranged in rows of 10. Although she shows an understanding of the problem and has a strategy for solving it, her strategy is not appropriate for students in Grade 3.

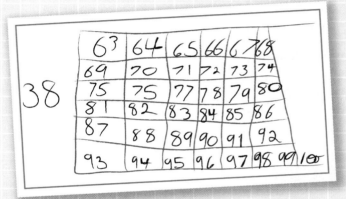

Bridget's Work

Students counting by 1s need more practice adding on and subtracting 10 and multiples of 10. They can benefit from continuing to play *Capture 5* and *Collect $2.00,* as well as solving practice problems that involve adding and subtracting multiples of 10. Help them use number lines and sticker place value sketches to solve these problems.

Problem 2: Representing a 2-Digit Number

Benchmark addressed (assessed at the end of the unit):

Benchmark 4: Break up 3-digit numbers less than 200 into 100s, 10s, and 1s in different ways (e.g., 153 equals 1 hundred, 5 tens, and 3 ones; 15 tens and 3 ones; 14 tens and 13 ones, and so on)

In order to meet the benchmark, students' work should show that they can:

- Find all possible combinations of dimes and pennies that equal 78¢;

- Write an accurate equation to represent each combination.

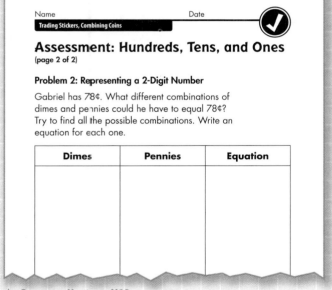

▲ Resource Masters, M22

Meeting the Benchmark

Students who find all possible combinations for 78¢ tend to be organized in their approach. Zhang, for example, started with 7 dimes and 8 pennies and then used one less dime each time. His work demonstrates the understanding that each time 1 less dime is used, 10 more pennies are added. He wrote equations that accurately represent each combination.

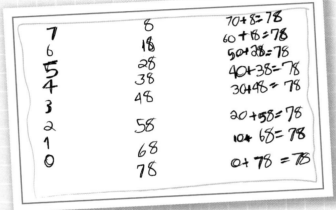

Zhang's Work

Partially Meeting the Benchmark

These students, like Jane, are able to correctly find at least three combinations, but do not find them all. These students are usually less organized in their approach, jumping from 7 dimes to 3 dimes to 6 dimes and so on. Ask these students to think about how to organize their work to prove that they have found all of the possible combinations.

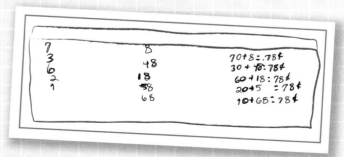

Jane's Work

Not Meeting the Benchmark

Some students are able to find only one or two combinations, or they may find a couple of correct combinations plus others that do not add to 78¢. Kim, for example, found two correct combinations (70 + 8, 50 + 28), but also incorrect combinations.

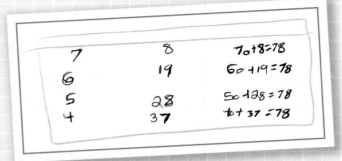

Kim's Work

Help these students use cubes or stickers to represent the 10s and 1s in the number and demonstrate what happens to the ones each time one less 10 is used. These students can benefit from practice constructing numbers with strips of 10 and singles. When they have gained confidence with representing 2-digit numbers in this way, they can practice making different combinations for the same number with problems such as those in the Daily Practice and Homework for Session 1.8.

Marisol interpreted this problem as asking for combinations of numbers that add to 78 and lost track of the context of dimes and pennies. Ask such students to read the problem to you and to restate it in their own words. When students have a correct understanding of the task, you can decide whether to give them another opportunity to solve the problem.

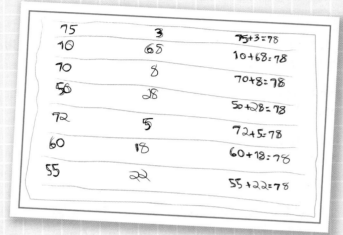

Marisol's Work

Learning the Addition Combinations

To develop efficient computation strategies, students need to become fluent with the addition combinations from $1 + 1$ to $10 + 10$. Fluency means that the combinations are quickly accessible, either because they are immediately known or because the calculation is so effortless as to be automatic (in the way that some adults quickly derive one combination from another; for example, thinking $8 + 9 = 8 + 10 - 1$). In *Investigations,* all students should be fluent with all of the addition combinations up to $10 + 10$ by the end of Grade 2. However, some students may need to review and practice some of these combinations in Grade 3.

Why Do We Call Them *Combinations*?

The addition problems from $1 + 1$ through $10 + 10$ are traditionally referred to as "addition facts." The *Investigations* curriculum follows the National Council of Teachers of Mathematics (NCTM) convention of calling these expressions *combinations* rather than *facts* for two reasons. First, referring to *only* particular addition and multiplication combinations as *facts* seems to give them elevated status. This makes them seem more important than other critical parts of mathematics.

In addition, the word *fact* implies that something cannot be learned through reasoning. For example, it is a fact that the first president of the United States was George Washington, and it is a fact that Rosa Parks was born in Alabama in 1913. If these facts are important for us to know, we can remember them or use reference materials to look them up. However, the sum of $7 + 8$ can be determined in many ways; it is logically connected to our system of numbers and operations. If we forget the sum, but understand what addition is and know some related combinations, we can find the sum through reasoning. For example:

If we know that $7 + 7 = 14$, we can add 1 more to get 15.

If we know that $8 + 8 = 16$, we can subtract 1 to get 15.

If we know that $7 + 3 = 10$, we can then add the 5 that is left from the 8 to get 15. ($7 + 8 = 7 + 3 + 5 = 15$)

The term *facts* does convey a meaning that is generally understood by some students and family members, so you will need to decide whether to use the term *facts* along with *combinations* in certain settings in order to make your meaning clear. Further, it does not seem appropriate to refer to the counterparts for subtraction and division as "combinations," because subtraction and division do not involve the action of combining. Therefore, for convenience we refer to "subtraction facts" and "division facts."

Learning the Addition Combinations Fluently

The *Investigations* curriculum, like NCTM, recognizes the importance of students' learning the basic combinations fluently through reasoning about number relationships: "Fluency with whole-number computation depends, in large part, on fluency with basic number combinations— the single digit addition and multiplication pairs and their counterparts for subtraction and division. Fluency with basic number combinations develops from well-understood meanings for the four operations and from a focus on thinking strategies". . . . "[*Principles and Standards for School Mathematics,* pp. 152–153]"

In other words, students learn these combinations best by using strategies, not simply by rote memorization. Relying on memory alone is not sufficient. If you forget—as we all do at times—you are left with nothing. If, on the other hand, your learning is based on an understanding of numbers and their relationships, you have a way to rethink and restructure your knowledge when you do not remember something you thought you knew.

In Grade 2, students learned these combinations in groups (make-10 combinations; plus-1, -2, or -10 combinations; doubles and near-doubles), which helped them learn good strategies for solving them easily. Fluency develops through frequent and repeated use; therefore, as students worked on a particular category of combinations, they played games and engaged in activities that focused on those combinations. For example, students reviewed the combinations that make

10 by playing *Make 10* and *Tens Go Fish*. The Classroom Routine *Today's Number* provided another opportunity for practice.

Students in Grade 2 used Addition Cards to think about combinations they knew and to practice those they did not yet know. Over the year, students collected a set of Addition Cards for each category and sorted them into two envelopes: "Combinations I Know" and "Combinations I Am Still Working On." Students wrote clues on these cards to help them remember the combinations they found difficult.

$7 + 8$	$7 + 8$
$8 + 7$	$8 + 7$
Clue: Think 7 + 7 = 14	Clue: 7 + 3, then add 5 more

In Grade 3, students again use Addition Cards (M24–M28) as they review the addition combinations. At the beginning of Investigation 2, they sort these cards as they did in Grade 2 and focus on the combinations they have not yet learned. As you observe your students and assess their knowledge of combinations later in Investigation 2, you will note that some may need more practice in one or more of these categories, particularly the final group of remaining combinations. Addition Combinations Practice (M29) contains blank addition cards for you or students to fill in, according to their individual needs.

Knowing the addition combinations should be judged not only by quick recall but also by fluency in use. Can students call on these combinations and use them easily as they solve other problems? Through repeated use and familiarity, students will come to know most of the addition combinations quickly. For the others, they will be able to use some quick and comfortable strategy based on reasoning about the numbers.

Categories of Addition Combinations

The categories of combinations are listed below. There are also notes about when most students learn these combinations. Note that some combinations fall into more than one category. For example, 1 + 9 and 9 + 1 is both a combination that makes 10 and a plus-1 combination.

Plus-1 and plus-2 combinations Many students leave Grade 1 fluent with the combinations that involve adding 1 or 2 to any single-digit number (8 + 1 and 7 + 2). As second graders come to understand that addition is commutative, they also become fluent with combinations in which the order of the numbers is reversed (1 + 8 and 2 + 7).

Make-10 combinations These two-addend combinations of 10 (e.g., 3 + 7, 4 + 6) were a benchmark for the end of Grade 1; students review them in Grade 2.

Doubles By the end of first grade, many students know their doubles combinations up to 5 + 5. In Grade 2, students work on these combinations up to 10 + 10. Students practice these combinations throughout Grade 2 and should gain fluency with them by the end of the year.

Near doubles (or doubles plus or minus 1) Students learn these combinations in Grade 2—those that are one more or one less than the doubles (e.g., 5 + 6, 7 + 8)—by relating them to the doubles.

Plus-10 combinations As students work on ideas about place value in Grade 2, they learn the plus-10 combinations—the sums of 10 and the numbers 1–10 (10 + 1, 10 + 2, 10 + 3, . . . 10 + 10).

Plus-9 combinations Students learn these combinations—the sums of 9 and the numbers 1–10 (9 + 1, 9 + 2, 9 + 3, . . . 9 + 10)—by relating them to the plus-10 combinations.

Remaining combinations Students who are fluent with doubles plus or minus 1 may be able to use the "clue" that several of the remaining combinations are doubles *plus or minus 2*. Students who are fluent with the make-10 combinations and with breaking numbers apart can solve most of these quickly (e.g., by breaking apart 7 + 5 into 7 + 3 + 2). Similarly, students can use their knowledge of make-10 combinations to solve "near-10" combinations (6 + 3, 7 + 4, 8 + 3).

Assessment: Addition Combinations

As you observe the students during the Addition Combinations assessment, you will find that a student is likely to fall into one of the three following groups:

Fluent Students who are fluent with their addition combinations to 10 + 10 can hear or read a problem, think for a moment, and then say the answer. Most students in Grade 3 should be in this category.

Nearly fluent Students in this category are fluent with many of these combinations but pause to figure out the answer to some ("8 + 5 is 8 . . . 9, 10, 11, 12, 13"). Note which combinations still cause trouble, and check that these match the cards in students' envelopes of "Combinations I'm Still Working On." Also, point them out to students: "You've come a long way with these combinations, but a few of them still seem to give you some trouble. How could we make it easier for you to remember that 8 + 5 and 5 + 8 equal 13?"

Continued practice with the activities described below will help these students become fluent. You can also use Addition Combinations Practice (M29) to assign students particular combinations to work on each week until they know them all.

Not yet fluent These students need to figure out many of these problems, using their fingers to count up or using cubes to model the problem. At Grade 3, there should be very few students in this category. They need more intensive practice with many or all of the activities described below.

Helping the "Nearly Fluent" Students

Students who are nearly fluent need more practice. They should use their Addition Cards to practice the combinations they are still working on. Work with them to write clues that they find helpful.

The categories listed below are likely to require further practice. Along with Addition Card practice, students will benefit from activities focused on these categories. Note that when students are relating one category of combinations to another, modeling the relationship between these combinations with cubes and on the number line is particularly important.

Near-doubles Arrange small-group work that helps students connect the near-doubles to the doubles combinations. Have them use cubes and the number line.

Plus-10 combinations Have students use concrete models to examine what happens when 10 is added to a number. Give students the opportunity to solve plus-10 problems by using the 100 chart, a number line, and cubes (with some in towers of 10).

Plus-9 combinations Arrange small-group work that helps students connect the plus-9 combinations to the plus-10 combinations. Have them use cubes and the number line.

Remaining combinations Arrange small-group work that helps students connect the remaining combinations to other categories (for example, relating the plus-8 combinations to the plus-9 and plus-10 combinations; the doubles plus or minus 2 combinations to the doubles; and combinations such as 3 + 6, 3 + 8, and 4 + 7 to the make-10 combinations). Have them use cubes and the number line.

Helping the "Not Yet Fluent" Students

Students who are not yet fluent may need practice with the above categories, as well as with some or all of the categories listed below. They can benefit from further experience with games and activities from the Grade 1 and 2 *Investigations* units. If you have access to these units, you will find the complete descriptions and recording sheets for each game or activity in the units named below. If you cannot get these, use the descriptions to design similar activities.

Many of these activities use the sets of Primary Number Cards, which, unlike the Digit Cards, include the number 10. Try to borrow or copy some sets of these cards, or consider using decks of regular playing cards with the jacks, queens, and kings removed.

Plus-1 and plus-2 combinations The game *Plus 1 or 2 Bingo* (from Grade 2 *Counting, Coins, and Combinations*) provides practice with these combinations. Players have a 6 × 6 gameboard with the numbers 1–12 placed randomly in the squares. With the goal of covering an entire row, the student chooses a Number Card, adds 1 or 2 to that number, and covers that total. Including wild cards encourages students to work backward: "If I want to cover 8, what number should I make this wild card be?"

For many students, the most difficult combinations are those in which the first addend is 1 or 2 (1 + 8 or 2 + 7). These students need time to make sense of why 8 + 1 and 1 + 8 have the same sum. You can work with a student or a small group to think about this idea. For example, pose two related story problems that use the same numbers. Have a collection of cubes or counters available for students to use to model what is happening from problem to problem.

I bought 1 red apple and 6 green apples at the store. How many apples did I buy?

The next day I went back and I bought 6 red apples and 1 green apple. How many apples did I buy that day?

Encourage students to explain their thinking and to use cubes to model their strategies.

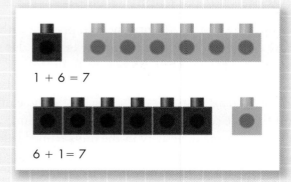

1 + 6 = 7

6 + 1 = 7

"It's 6 and 1 and 1 and 6. It's still 7 altogether."

"It doesn't matter which order you count it in, it's still 7."

"You didn't add any more or take any away, so it's still 7."

For further practice, pose similar questions based on different contexts:

What if I were playing a game that involves rolling two number cubes? I rolled a 1 and a 5. How many altogether? What if I said I rolled a 5 and 1?

What about a game that uses the Digit Cards? I turned over two cards. I got an 8 and a 1. How many altogether? This time I got a 1 and an 8. Now how many?

The Combinations That Make 10

All of the following games and activities provide good practice with make-10 combinations.

Make 10 (from Grade 2, *Counting, Coins, and Combinations*) Cards are arranged in four rows of five, face up. Players take turns finding two cards that equal 10 when added together.

Tens Go Fish (from Grade 2, *Counting, Coins, and Combinations*) Each player is dealt five cards. Players take turns asking each other for cards that, when combined with a card in their hand, will total 10.

Today's Number: 10 (Classroom Routine in Grade 2) Students generate equivalent expressions for a particular number. Encourage them to use addition and only two addends.

How Many of Each? problems (from Grade 1, *How Many of Each, Solving Story Problems,* and *Number Games and Crayon Puzzles*) This recurring problem in Grade 1 is set up as follows: "You have 10 toys. Some are blocks, and some are marbles. How many of each could you have?" Give students these problems with different contexts (blocks and marbles, apples and oranges, peas and carrots) to provide additional practice.

Heads and Tails (from Grade 1, *How Many of Each?*) Students have a 2-column table labeled "Heads" and "Tails." They drop 10 pennies and record the number that land with heads and tails facing up. You can also use 2-sided chips or beans that have been painted two colors. Students can also play *On and Off,* recording the number that fall on and off a piece of paper.

How Many Am I Hiding? (from Grade 1, *How Many of Each, Solving Story Problems,* and *Number Games and Crayon Puzzles*) Make a tower of 10 cubes and show it to the student. Agree that there are 10 cubes. Then ask the student to close his or her eyes. Break off some cubes and hide them behind your back. Now show the student the cubes you did not hide. "How many am I hiding? How do you know?"

Counters in a Cup (from Grade 1, *Solving Story Problems* and *Number Games and Crayon Puzzles*) Show the student 10 counters (or chips, or pennies) and agree on the total. With the student covering his or her eyes, hide some of the items under a paper cup. "How many am I hiding? How do you know?"

Doubles

The following two activities are useful for practice with doubles:

Double It (from Grade 2, *Counting, Coins, and Combinations*) Students practice the doubles combinations by drawing a number card, doubling it, and recording the sum.

Doubles Arrays (from Grade 2, *Counting, Coins, and Combinations*) Students draw a Number Card (or Digit Card) and color in double that number of squares on grid paper. They record an equation that illustrates the double.

End-of-Unit Assessment

Problem 1

Benchmark addressed:

Benchmark 3: Solve addition problems with 2-digit numbers using strategies that involve breaking numbers apart by place or adding one number in parts

In order to meet the benchmark, students' work should show that they can:

- Accurately combine two quantities by breaking the numbers apart by place and adding the sums of each place, or by adding one number to the other in parts;

- Show how they solved the problem;

- Include an equation that matches the situation.

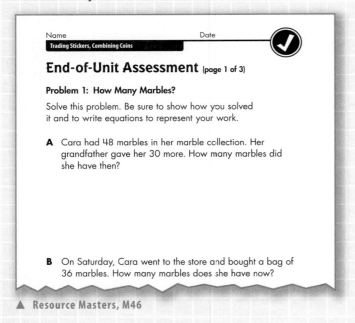

▲ Resource Masters, M46

Meeting the Benchmark

The following examples of student work provide typical responses for Problem 1. Both of these students met the benchmark—they were able to interpret the problem, solve it accurately, show their work, and write an equation.

Adding by Place

Gina solves the first part of the problem by adding tens and ones. She breaks 48 into 40 + 8, combines 40 + 30 to make 70, and then adds 8 to get a sum of 78.

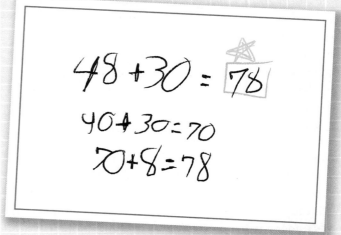

Gina's Work

To solve the second part of the problem, she breaks 78 and 36 into tens and ones, combines the tens and ones, and adds the sum to get 114.

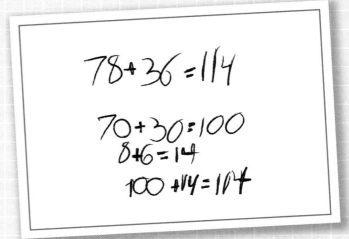

Gina's Work

Adding One Number in Parts

Denzel solves this problem by starting with 48 and adding the 30 on in one chunk. He solved this part of the problem mentally.

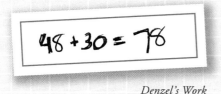

Denzel's Work

To solve the second part of the problem, he adds 78 + 30, then adds 2 (from 6 = 2 + 4) to get to 110, and then adds 4 to get to 114.

Denzel's Work

Although most third graders at this time of the year use one of these two strategies, you might have a student or two who have other good strategies they use to solve the problem accurately. For example: "I took 2 from 36 and made 78 into 80, and then I added 80 and 34. So 80 and 30 is 110, and 4 more is 114." These students also meet the benchmark.

Partially Meeting the Benchmark

Some students understand the structure of the problem—that it is about combining two groups and finding the total—but make errors as they add or attempt to keep track of the quantities in the problem. For example, a student might correctly break up both numbers into tens and ones but leave out one of the parts when adding them back together. After you review their work, ask these students to look for and correct such errors on their own. Encourage them to take their time and work carefully to avoid similar

errors in the future. In addition, note whether these kinds of errors are consistent across problems. If they are, what is causing the difficulty? Is the student losing track of the parts of the numbers? Does the student know how to add multiples of 10? Does the student know the basic addition combinations?

Other students understand the structure of the problem and how to solve it but struggle with how to adequately show their work. Ask these students to tell you how they solved the problem in order to probe their understanding. Then encourage them to add to their written explanation as appropriate. Note that they need more support in finding ways to show their work.

Not Meeting the Benchmark

Students who solve the problem by counting all, as Benjamin did, do not meet the benchmark. By Grade 3, students should be adding more efficiently. These students do interpret the situation successfully, recognizing that the problem requires combining two amounts. However, they need support in thinking about the composition of the numbers in the problem and how this can help them break the numbers into parts that are easy to add. Ask these students to represent the numbers with place value materials (cubes or stickers) and to show you what happens when they combine the tens and ones from each number or when they add tens first and then ones to one of the numbers.

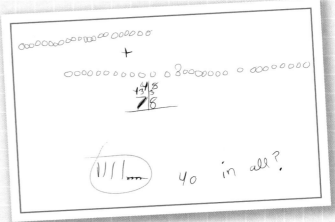

Benjamin's Work

Problem 2

Benchmark addressed:

Benchmark 5: Find combinations of 2-digit numbers that equal 100 or $1.00

In order to meet the benchmark, students' work should show that they can:

- Create two 2-digit numbers from the cards shown that add to 100, using a strategy that involves knowledge of place value or using known combinations of 100 to create a related pair that also adds to 100;

- Clearly explain their strategies.

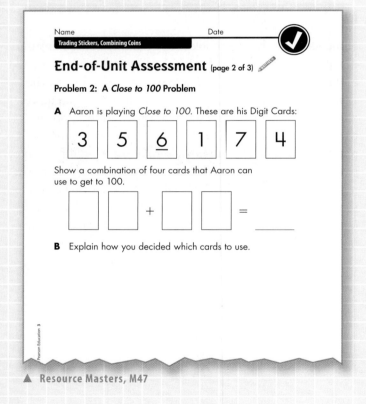

▲ Resource Masters, M47

Meeting the Benchmark

Bridget is typical of students who meet the benchmark. She used the strategy of choosing two cards to make 90 for the tens digits and two cards to make 10 with the ones digits.

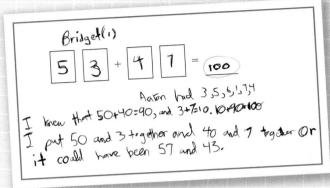

Bridget's Work

Partially Meeting the Benchmark

Jung is a student who partially met the benchmark. She made two numbers that added to 105. Her explanation shows that she used knowledge of place value to choose two cards for the tens digits to create a combination (70 + 30) that adds to 100. However, she failed to consider the effect of the ones digits on the sum when choosing the digits for the tens place.

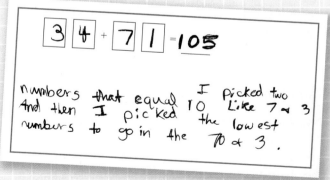

Jung's Work

Ask students such as Jung questions to help them consider both the tens and ones digits as they choose which cards to use. For example: "I notice that you started by making 100 with the tens digits. What happened when you added the digits in the ones place? What if one of your numbers is 57? What should your other number be? What is the sum of the tens digits? Why does it work to have only 90 in the tens digits, not 100?"

Oscar also partially met the benchmark. He created two numbers that added to 99, but wrote no explanation of how he chose which cards to use. Ask students who got close to 100, but failed to write an explanation, to explain to you how they chose their cards. Help them think about how to clearly record an explanation.

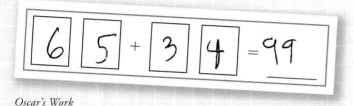

Oscar's Work

Not Meeting the Benchmark

Students who did not meet the benchmark either created a pair of 2-digit numbers that added to a sum far from 100 or failed to answer the question at all. Elena created two numbers that added to 121 and failed to use knowledge of place value or known combinations to choose which cards to use.

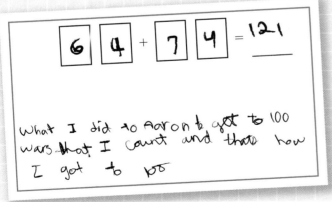

Elena's Work

With students whose combinations were far from 100, help them by making the first number for them and asking them what they need to consider as they look for the digits

to use for the second number. They can model this with sticker place value sketches, first adding strips of 10 to get close to 100 and then adding on singles.

Problem 3

Benchmark addressed:

Benchmark 4: Break up 3-digit numbers less than 200 into 100s, 10s, and 1s in different ways (e.g., 153 equals 1 hundred, 5 tens, and 3 ones; 15 tens and 3 ones; 14 tens and 13 ones, and so on)

In order to meet the benchmark, students' work should show that they can:

- Find at least 4 combinations of hundreds, tens, and ones that equal 172;

- Find at least 4 combinations of tens and ones that equal 172;

- Write an accurate equation to represent each combination.

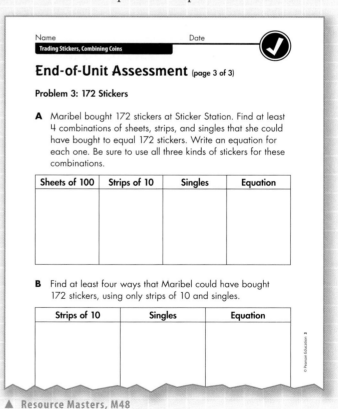

▲ **Resource Masters, M48**

Meeting the Benchmark

Students who find at least four combinations of 172 stickers that use sheets of 100, strips of 10, and singles and at least four that use only strips and singles tend to be organized in their approach. Becky, for example, started with 1 sheet, 7 strips, and 2 singles and then used one less strip of 10 each time. Her work demonstrates understanding that each time one less strip of 10 is used, 10 more singles are added. She used a similar approach for the combinations including only strips of 10 and singles. She wrote equations that accurately represent each combination.

Becky's Work

Partially Meeting the Benchmark

Some of these students, such as Jane, correctly find some combinations of 172 stickers but cannot easily generate four different combinations. They are not fluent in thinking about equivalent ways to represent a quantity by using 100s by 10s, and 1s.

Jane's Work

Jane also has an error in one of her equations. She writes $0 + 16 + 12 = 172$. This may be a simple error that she would correct easily, if asked to double-check her equation, or it may indicate that she is not confident in thinking about the value of 16 strips of ten. If she has to carefully compute each time she has a number of 10s (perhaps by counting up by 10), thinking this through more slowly may also account for generating fewer combinations for 172.

Jane can benefit from continuing to work on story problems that involve strips of 10 and singles in the sticker context, such as those for Investigation 1 in the *Student Activity Book.*

Not Meeting the Benchmark

These students may find a few correct combinations but make errors that signify a lack of understanding of the equivalence of 1 hundred and 10 tens and of 1 ten and 10 ones. Although Nicholas starts with one correct combination (17 strips and 2 singles), he increases the number of singles by 1 instead of 10 each time he uses one fewer strip of 10, so the subsequent combinations are not correct. He is able to make only one combination with a sheet of 100 by breaking up 172 by place (1 hundred, 7 strips of 10, 2 singles).

Sheets of 100	Strips of 10	Singles	Equation
100	7	2	

Strips of 10	Singles	Equation
17 16 15	2 3 4	

Nicholas's Work

It may be that Nicholas has learned that one way to make a correct combination of stickers is to use the digits in order—1 in the first column, 7 in the second column, 2 in the third column—without understanding what each digit represents.

Students such as Nicholas need more experience using tools, such as cubes organized in towers of 10, to create quantities (show 72 with cubes), to add quantities (add 36 + 76, using cubes), and to find a missing part (if you have 36 cubes and need 100, how many more do you need?). Help them use sticker place value sketches to represent their work. The Daily Practice pages in the Grade 3 unit *Surveys and Line Plots* will be helpful for these students; you may want to create additional practice for them at this time that is based on those practice pages. A priority for these students is to work on combinations of quantities that add to 100. They can benefit from continuing to play *Close to 100* and *Make a Dollar,* using cubes or coins to model their moves during the game.

Dialogue Box

Adding 10s

Students in this classroom have just added the series of numbers below. They are discussing the pattern they notice and why it occurs.

$$36 + 10 = 46$$

$$46 + 10 = 56$$

$$56 + 10 = 66$$

Oscar points to the answers on the chart paper and shows that the ones column always has a six and that the number in the tens place increases by one each time.

Oscar: See, the tens numbers go 4, 5, 6 and the ones place stays 6 every time.

Teacher: Oscar has noticed an interesting pattern. Can anyone say why this is happening?

Kathryn: I took the 36 and put the ten on, but I didn't take the 6 away.

Nicholas: It's like skip counting by 1s in the tens place.

Deondra gathers cubes to show what is happening as 10s are added to a number. She holds up three towers of 10 cubes and then one more tower of 10.

Deondra: I can show it with cubes. This is 30 (the three towers) and this is 10 (the one tower) and that equals forty.

Deondra lays the cubes side by side. She then adds 6 cubes to the 3 towers of ten.

Deondra: I put back the 6 from the 36, and then I had 46 cubes.

Teacher: So when you added 10 to 36, the tens place went up by one and the ones place stayed the same. Do you think this will be true when you add 10 to any 2-digit number? Think more about this pattern as you do the problems on the student sheet.

After solving the problems on *Student Activity Book* pages 1–4, the students come back together to discuss Problem 5.

$$27 + 10 = \underline{\hspace{1cm}}$$

$$37 + 10 = \underline{\hspace{1cm}}$$

$$47 + 20 = \underline{\hspace{1cm}}$$

Teacher: What did you notice when you solved these problems? What happened when you added 10 to 2-digit numbers?

Jung: The same pattern happened. The tens place got one bigger and the ones place stayed the same.

Teacher: Jung, can you use cubes or sketches of stickers to show why this happens?

Jung: *(drawing two strips of 10 and 7 singles)* I start with 27 stickers. Every time you draw another strip of 10 *(Jung draws more strips of 10 as she speaks),* you go up 10 more: 27 to 37, 37 to 47, 47 to 57. The numbers get higher by 10. I didn't add any singles, so the ones place stayed the same.

Teacher: What did you notice about the third problem, 47 + 20?

Edwin: The tens place goes up by 2, but you're still not changing the ones.

Teacher: So the amount goes from 47 to 67. Is the amount changing by 2?

Edwin: It's really 20 because you're adding two 10s.

The students in this class have noticed the patterns of the tens place going up by one and the ones place remaining the same every time a 10 is added to a number. By using cubes and sketches of stickers to represent the action of these problems, they are able to explain how the digits of the numbers represent the changes in quantity.

Strategies for *Capture 5*

Near the beginning of Investigation 1, Session 7, students are discussing the combinations of Change Cards they can use to move a game piece from 34 to capture a chip on 56. After looking at two sets of Change Cards, they have shared the following combinations:

$$34 + 20 + 2 = 56$$

$$34 + 10 + 10 + 2 = 56$$

$$34 + 30 - 10 + 2 = 56$$

$$34 + 30 - 10 + 3 - 1 = 56$$

Teacher: I'm interested in hearing how you figured out what cards to choose.

Becky: I knew that I had to move 22 spaces to get the chip on 56, so I looked for cards that equaled 22. I used the +10, +10, and +2 cards, because they make 22.

Teacher: So Becky looked for cards to equal 22. Do people agree that the distance between 34 and 56 is 22 spaces? (*Students indicate their agreement.*) Let's think about the other equations up here. Can you see 22 in those equations also?

Ines: The first one. (*Ines points to the first equation written on the chart.*) It says 34 plus 20 plus 2 equals 56. 20 plus 2 is 22.

Teacher: What about this one? (*The teacher points to the third equation.*)

Keisha: That one's 22, too. 30 − 10 is 20, and then 2 more is 22.

Jung: Every equation really proves it, because when you add all the numbers up, they all equal 22.

Dwayne: I found another way to get to 56.
$$34 + 10 + 1 + 10 + 1 = 56.$$

Teacher: How much did you move from 34 to 56?

Dwayne: I moved 22 spaces. The +10 gets you to 44 and +1 gets to 45. Then +10 gets to 55, and +1 gets to 56. The two 10s make 20, and the two 1s make 2. That's 22.

Teacher: Can we go back and prove that the moves in this last equation ($34 + 30 - 10 + 3 - 1 = 56$) equal 22?

Kathryn: I added 30 to 34 and that got me to 64, and then I subtracted 10 and got to 54. Then +3 got me to 57, and −1 got me to 56. The 30 minus the 10 is 20, and the 3 minus the 1 is 2. That's 22.

In this discussion, the teacher recognizes the importance of Becky's strategy of first identifying the distance between the game piece and the target number and then looking for combinations of Change Cards that equal that amount. She therefore decides to pursue it with the class. This pushes students to think about the relationship between their moves in *Capture 5* and the difference between their starting and ending numbers. The teacher will observe whether more students use this relationship as they return to playing the game in Math Workshop.

Dialogue Box

Strategies for *Close to 100*

As students shared the strategies they were using for choosing numbers in the *Close to 100* game, the teacher posted their ideas on chart paper.

Teacher: Think about how you chose numbers to try. Do you have any advice for your friends on how to get close to 100? Tell me something that *you* look for when you try to get close to 100.

Elena: I first try to find two numbers that equal 10, like 7 and 3, or 6 and 4.

Teacher: For the tens digit?

Elena: Yes.

Oscar: I'd look for 9, and put another number with it, and it might come close to 100.

Teacher: When you started with 9, was it on the tens side or the ones side?

Oscar: On the tens side, so it's 90.

Teacher: So you started with 90? What else did you look at?

Oscar: I tried to get 10 on the ones side.

Gil: I tried to find a high number and then a little one, like 90-something, and then if I had a zero, I made something like zero five (05).

Teacher: So you tried to make something in the 90s and a 1-digit number.

Beatriz: I tried to find a way to get 9, and then I tried to find a way to make 10.

Teacher: So you tried to find two numbers that you could use in the tens place to make 90 and two numbers to make 10?

Beatriz: Yes, I make 9 with the first two numbers [meaning the tens digits; for example, 70 and 20, or 80 and 10]. Then I try to make 10 with the second two. I don't want to make the first two equal 10 because then I would already have 100 [$70 + 30 = 100$], and you hardly ever get two zeros. So, I try to get numbers that make 9 instead of 10, and then I try to make 10 in the ones place.

Teacher: Did anyone think about the combinations to make 100 that you already know and use those to choose your cards?

Denzel: I didn't have 20 + 80, which I know is 100, so I did 21 plus 83 because that was the closest I could get. I made 83 + 21 and that was 104.

Deondra: I know that 60 plus 40 equals 100. I had the cards to make 62. That's 2 more than 60, so I looked to see if I could make a number 2 less than 40. I couldn't make 38, so I made 37. 62 plus 37 got me to 99.

To prepare for this discussion, the teacher walked around the classroom while students were playing *Close to 100* and noted two main strategies: using digits in the tens place to make 90 and in the ones place to make 10, and starting with known combinations and adjusting the numbers. Her goal in this discussion was to highlight both of these approaches. When no student described starting with known combinations, she explicitly asked whether anyone had used this approach.

Dialogue Box

Strategies for *Make a Dollar*

Students are playing *Make a Dollar*. The teacher circulates, observing the students and asking them to articulate the strategies they are using as they play. She stops to talk to Benjamin and Gil to find out how they are choosing their cards.

Benjamin: I am thinking about this one and something else (points to a card with 70 cents).

Benjamin quickly finds the match to his card.

Benjamin: 70 and 30. That makes a dollar.

Teacher: Are you using any strategies that help you while you are playing?

Benjamin: I'm starting by finding the amount on one card and then looking for a card that helps it make one dollar.

Benjamin finds a card worth 80 cents and then quickly notices another card that has four nickels. He grabs that pair.

Gil: I don't see any more cards that match. Oh wait! I see one! I see one! Nope, only 90 cents!

The boys work together for about three minutes to try and find another pair. Then they replace the four cards Benjamin used, and Gil takes his turn.

Gil: I found one. Wait. I want to count the coins and make sure it's right.

Gil starts with the card that equals 50 cents (two quarters). Then he counts the card with one quarter.

Gil: This doesn't work. It is only 75. We need to put the cards back.

The two boys continue working cooperatively to find matches for Gil. At another desk, Becky and Pilar are also playing *Make a Dollar*. Becky has a card with 60 cents on it.

Teacher: What are you looking for?

Becky: I knew that this was 60 because I counted the quarter, then the nickel and that makes thirty. Then I counted the three dimes. It makes 60. So I knew that I had to find 40.

Teacher: So you used 60 plus 40 equals 100 to help you. How does 60 plus 40 equals 100 help you figure out how much to add to 60¢ to make a dollar?

Becky: I know that a dollar is equal to 100 cents, so 60 cents plus 40 cents is 100 cents and that's a dollar.

Pilar: These cards aren't tricky if you add them up the right way.

Teacher: What do you mean?

Pilar: I start with the largest coins like 50 cents and then go down. If there are quarters and nickels, I put those together because 30 is easier then 25.

Becky: I do it a little differently. I start with the largest coin, but then I look for other coins that are easy to add to it, like tens.

As the teacher circulates, she asks questions that give her information about how students determine the value of the coins on each card, and about the strategies they use to find pairs of cards that add to a dollar. The students verbalize a range of strategies, such as starting with the largest coin and then adding 10s, combining coins such as a quarter and a nickel to make an amount that's "easier to work with," and using known combinations that add to 100 to find pairs of cards that add to a dollar. Asking students to articulate their approaches helps consolidate these strategies and also encourages learning from others as they work toward greater computational fluency and efficiency. Working cooperatively on each player's turn also encourages conversation about the coin combinations and thus supports the learning.

Student Math Handbook

The *Student Math Handbook* pages related to this unit are pictured on the following pages. This book is designed to be used flexibly: as a resource for students doing classwork, as a book students can take home for reference while doing homework and playing math games with their families, and as a reference for families to better understand the work their children are doing in class.

When students take the *Student Math Handbook* home, they and their families can discuss these pages together to reinforce or enhance students' understanding of the mathematical concepts and games in this unit.

Representing Place Value

Math Words
· equation

Sticker Station is a place that sells stickers.

At Sticker Station you can buy single stickers, strips of ten stickers, or sheets of one hundred stickers.

1 sheet of one hundred	1 strip of ten	1 single
100 stickers	10 stickers	1 sticker

This is a quick way to record stickers.

1 sheet of one hundred   1 strip of ten   1 single

Look at this sketch of 125 stickers.

Equation: 100 + 20 + 5 = 125

How could you show 56 stickers? How could you show 141 stickers?

SMH
6 six

Place Value: Ones, Tens, and Hundreds
(page 1 of 2)

Math Words
· equal

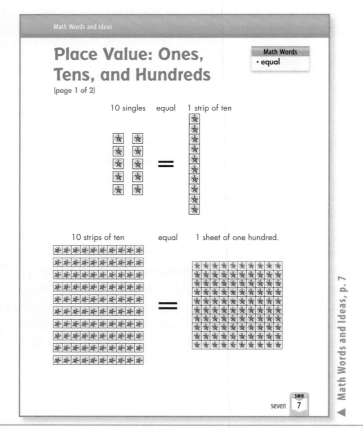

10 singles   equal   1 strip of ten

10 strips of ten   equal   1 sheet of one hundred.

seven SMH 7

Place Value: Ones, Tens, and Hundreds
(page 2 of 2)

Jessica and Carlos went to Sticker Station. They each bought 57 stickers.

Jessica bought 5 strips of ten and 7 single stickers.

Equation:
50 + 7 = 57

Carlos bought 4 strips of ten and 17 single stickers.

Equation:
40 + 17 = 57

1 strip of ten equals 10 singles.

Kevin and Mia went to Sticker Station. They each bought 128 stickers.

Kevin bought 1 sheet of one hundred, 2 strips of ten, and 8 single stickers.

Equation:
100 + 20 + 8 = 128

Mia bought 12 strips of ten and 8 single stickers.

Equation:
120 + 8 = 128

1 sheet of one hundred equals 10 strips of ten.

Suppose that you went to Sticker Station and also bought 128 stickers. What are some other ways you could buy 128 stickers?

SMH
8 eight

Place Value: Many Ways to Make 145

Four students went to Sticker Station. Each of them bought 145 stickers.

Student	Sheets of 100	Strips of 10	Singles	Equation
Gina bought these stickers.	1	4	5	100 + 40 + 5 = **145**
Adam bought these stickers.	0	14	5	0 + 140 + 5 = **145**
Denzel bought these stickers.	0	13	15	0 + 130 + 15 = **145**
Pilar bought these stickers.	0	12	25	0 + 120 + 25 = **145**

 Suppose that you went to Sticker Station and also bought 145 stickers. What are some other ways you could buy 145 stickers?

nine **9** SMH

◀ Math Words and Ideas, p. 9

Place Value: Ones, Tens, Hundreds, and Thousands (page 1 of 2)

Math Words
• place value
• ones
• tens
• hundreds
• thousands
• digit

The value of a digit changes depending on its place in a number.

| thousands | , | hundreds | tens | ones |

In these two examples the digit 4 has different values.

The digit 4 in the tens place represents 40.

The Brooks family drove 1,940 miles last summer when they traveled to the Grand Canyon.

The digit 4 in the hundreds place represents 400.

Casawn has 408 car stickers in his collection.

Casawn's stickers

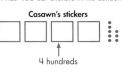

4 hundreds

SMH **10** ten

◀ Math Words and Ideas, p. 10

Place Value: Ones, Tens, Hundreds, and Thousands (page 2 of 2)

Look at the values of the digits in these numbers.

> 408 (four hundred eight)
>
> The digit 4 represents 400.
> The digit 0 represents 0 (tens).
> The digit 8 represents 8.
>
> 400 + 0 + 8 = 408

> 1,940 (one thousand, nine hundred forty)
>
> The digit 1 represents 1,000.
> The digit 9 represents 900.
> The digit 4 represents 40.
> The digit 0 represents 0 (ones).
>
> 1,000 + 900 + 40 + 0 = 1,940

 What are the values of the digits in these numbers?
325   1,867

eleven **11** SMH

◀ Math Words and Ideas, p. 11

An Addition Situation

In this addition problem, two groups of stickers are combined or joined.

Arthur went to Sticker Station and bought 36 soccer stickers and 44 animal stickers. How many stickers did he buy altogether?

soccer stickers   animal stickers

These equations go with this problem.

$$36 + 44 = ?$$
$$44 + 36 = ?$$

SMH **12** twelve

◀ Math Words and Ideas, p. 12

Math Words and Ideas

Tools to Represent Addition Problems (page 1 of 3)

On the next few pages, you will see some of the tools you can use to represent addition problems such as this one.

Arthur went to Sticker Station and bought 36 soccer stickers and 44 animal stickers. How many stickers did he buy altogether?

$$36 + 44 = 80$$

Cubes

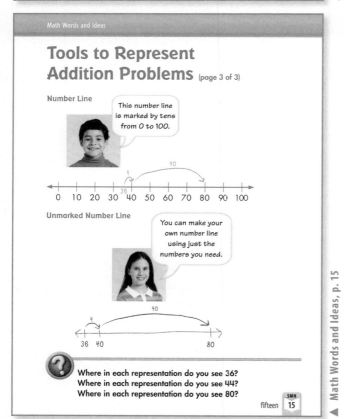

Coins

thirteen **SMH 13**

◀ Math Words and Ideas, p. 13

Math Words and Ideas

Tools to Represent Addition Problems (page 2 of 3)

100 Chart

1	2	3	4	5	6	7	8	9	10	
11	12	13	14	15	16	17	18	19	20	
21	22	23	24	25	26	27	28	29	30	
31	32	33	34	35	36	37	38	39	40	+4
41	42	43	44	45	46	47	48	49	50	+10
51	52	53	54	55	56	57	58	59	60	+10
61	62	63	64	65	66	67	68	69	70	+10
71	72	73	74	75	76	77	78	79	80	+10
81	82	83	84	85	86	87	88	89	90	
91	92	93	94	95	96	97	98	99	100	

SMH 14 fourteen

◀ Math Words and Ideas, p. 14

Math Words and Ideas

Tools to Represent Addition Problems (page 3 of 3)

Number Line

This number line is marked by tens from 0 to 100.

40

4

36

0 10 20 30 40 50 60 70 80 90 100

Unmarked Number Line

You can make your own number line using just the numbers you need.

40

4

36 40   80

? Where in each representation do you see 36?
Where in each representation do you see 44?
Where in each representation do you see 80?

fifteen **SMH 15**

◀ Math Words and Ideas, p. 15

Math Words and Ideas

Addition Combinations

Math Words
• sum

(page 1 of 4)

One of your goals in math class this year is to review and practice all the addition combinations up to 10 + 10.

10 + 10 =

2 + 7 =
7 + 2 =

3 + 3 =

4 + 6 =
6 + 4 =

5 + 8 =
8 + 5 =

Learning Two Combinations at a Time

These two problems look different, but they have the same sum.

8 + 3   3 + 8

When you know that 8 + 3 = 11, you also know that 3 + 8 = 11.

You've learned two addition combinations!

? Why do these two problems have the same answer?
7 + 2 = 9   2 + 7 = 9

SMH 16 sixteen

◀ Math Words and Ideas, p. 16

Addition Combinations

(page 2 of 4)

A helpful way to learn addition combinations is to think about one category at a time. Here are some categories you may have seen before. You probably already know many of these combinations.

Make 10 Combinations

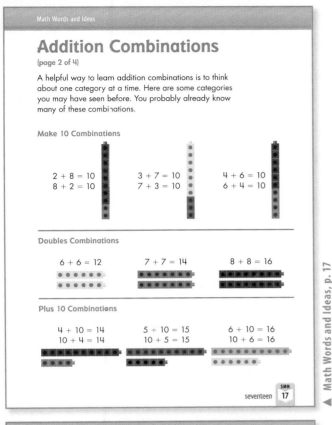

$2 + 8 = 10$
$8 + 2 = 10$

$3 + 7 = 10$
$7 + 3 = 10$

$4 + 6 = 10$
$6 + 4 = 10$

Doubles Combinations

$6 + 6 = 12$

$7 + 7 = 14$

$8 + 8 = 16$

Plus 10 Combinations

$4 + 10 = 14$
$10 + 4 = 14$

$5 + 10 = 15$
$10 + 5 = 15$

$6 + 10 = 16$
$10 + 6 = 16$

seventeen **SMH 17**

◀ Math Words and Ideas, p. 17

Addition Combinations

(page 3 of 4)

Here are some more categories to help you learn more of the addition combinations.

Near-Doubles Combinations

Some combinations are close to a doubles combination you know. Here are two examples.

Doubles minus 1	Doubles plus 1
$6 + 7 =$ $7 + 6 =$	$7 + 8 =$ $8 + 7 =$
Think: $7 + 7 - 1$	Think: $7 + 7 + 1$
-1	$+1$
$7 + 6 = (7 + 7) - 1 = $ **13**	$7 + 8 = (7 + 7) + 1 = $ **15**

Plus 9 Combinations

You can learn some combinations by relating them to a plus 10 combination you know. Here are two examples.

$5 + 9 =$ $9 + 5 =$	
Think: $9 + 1 + 4$	Think: $10 + 5 - 1$
	-1
$9 + 5 = 10 + 4 = $ **14**	$9 + 5 = (10 + 5) - 1 = $ **14**

SMH 18 eighteen

◀ Math Words and Ideas, p. 18

Addition Combinations

(page 4 of 4)

As you practice all the addition combinations, there will be some that you "just know" and others that you are "working on." To practice combinations that are difficult for you to remember, think of a combination that you know as a clue to help you.

Here are some examples. Gil and Ines have different clues to help them solve $5 + 7$.

Gil: I think of $7 + 7$, and then subtract 2.

$5 + 7 =$
$7 + 5 =$
Clue: $7 + 7 - 2$

Ines: First I add $5 + 5$, and then add 2 more.

$5 + 7 =$
$7 + 5 =$
Clue: $5 + 5 + 2$

Do you know these combinations or are you learning them?

$\begin{array}{r} 5 \\ +7 \\ \hline \end{array}$ $\begin{array}{r} 8 \\ +6 \\ \hline \end{array}$ $\begin{array}{r} 7 \\ +4 \\ \hline \end{array}$

nineteen **SMH 19**

◀ Math Words and Ideas, p. 19

Strategies for Solving Addition Problems (page 1 of 5)

There are different ways to solve addition problems.

Adding by Place

Gina used adding by place to solve this problem.

Bridget went to Sticker Station and bought 46 horse stickers and 74 space stickers. How many stickers did she buy altogether?

Gina's Solution

First I added the tens.	$40 + 70 = 110$
Then, I added the ones.	$6 + 4 = 10$
Then, I put the tens and ones together.	$110 + 10 = $ **120**

Gina's solution can also be shown using sticker sketches.

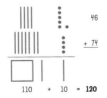

46
+ 74

$110 + 10 = $ **120**

I traded 10 strips for a sheet and 10 singles for a strip, so I have 1 sheet and 2 strips.

SMH 20 twenty

◀ Math Words and Ideas, p. 20

Math Words and Ideas

Strategies for Solving Addition Problems (page 2 of 5)

Ines and Philip used adding by place when they solved this problem.

$$258$$
$$+ 392$$

They added the hundreds together, the tens together, and the ones together. Their solutions are similar, but they recorded their work differently.

Ines's Solution

$200 + 300 = 500$

$50 + 90 = 140$

$8 + 2 = 10$

$500 + 140 + 10 =$ **650**

Philip's Solution

$$258$$
$$+ 392$$
$$\overline{500}$$
$$140$$
$$+\ 10$$
$$\overline{650}$$

Ines recorded her solution sideways and Philip recorded his up and down.

? How would you solve these problems?

$$37 + 86 \qquad \begin{array}{r} 463 \\ + 279 \end{array}$$

twenty-one **SMH 21**

◀ Math Words and Ideas, p. 21

Math Words and Ideas

Strategies for Solving Addition Problems (page 3 of 5)

Adding One Number in Parts

Bridget went to Sticker Station and bought 46 horse stickers and 74 space stickers. How many stickers did she buy altogether?

Edwin solved the problem by starting at 74 on the number line and adding 46 in parts.

Edwin's Solution

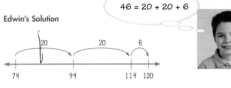

$46 = 20 + 20 + 6$

First I added on the 40 from 46 in jumps of 20.

$74 + 20 = 94$
$94 + 20 = 114$

Then I added the 6.

$114 + 6 = 120$

? Is there another way you could solve this problem by adding one number in parts?

SMH 22 twenty-two

◀ Math Words and Ideas, p. 22

Math Words and Ideas

Strategies for Solving Addition Problems (page 4 of 5)

$$258$$
$$+ 392$$

Kenji solved this problem by starting at 258 and adding 392 in parts.

Kenji's Solution

$$392 = 300 + 90 + 2$$

First I added the 300. $258 + 300 = 558$
Then I added the 90. $558 + 90 = 648$
Then I added the 2. $648 + 2 =$ **650**

Benjamin solved this problem by starting at 392 and adding 258 in parts.

Benjamin's Solution

$$258 = 8 + 250$$

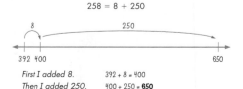

First I added 8. $392 + 8 = 400$
Then I added 250. $400 + 250 =$ **650**

twenty-three **SMH 23**

◀ Math Words and Ideas, p. 23

Math Words and Ideas

Strategies for Solving Addition Problems (page 5 of 5)

Changing the Numbers

Bridget went to Sticker Station and bought 46 horse stickers and 74 space stickers. How many stickers did she buy altogether?

Kathryn solved this problem by changing one number.

Kathryn's Solution

$46 + 4 = 50$

I added 4 to 46 to make 50. 50 is a "landmark" number, so it's easier for me to work with.

$$74$$
$$+ 50$$ I added 50 instead of 46.
$$\overline{124}$$
$$-\ 4$$ Then I subtracted the extra 4.
$$\overline{120}$$

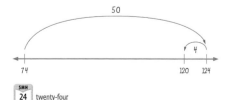

SMH 24 twenty-four

◀ Math Words and Ideas, p. 24

Math Words and Ideas

Tools to Represent Subtraction Problems (page 1 of 2)

On this page and the next, you will see some of the tools you can use to represent subtraction problems such as this one.

Ms. Santos's class is collecting cans for a recycling project. Their goal is to collect 175 cans. They have collected 63 cans so far. How many more cans do they need to collect to reach their goal?

$$63 + \underline{112} = 175 \text{ or}$$
$$175 - 63 = \underline{112}$$

Sticker Sketch

The answer is 112, the number of stickers that are left.

Number Line

112

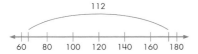

60   80   100   120   140   160   180

The answer is 112, the distance shown on the number line between the numbers 63 and 175.

twenty-nine   **SMH 29**

▲ Math Words and Ideas, p. 29

Math Words and Ideas

Tools to Represent Subtraction Problems (page 2 of 2)

200 Chart

1	2	3	4	5	6	7	8	9	10
11	12	13	14	15	16	17	18	19	20
21	22	23	24	25	26	27	28	29	30
31	32	33	34	35	36	37	38	39	40
41	42	43	44	45	46	47	48	49	50
51	52	53	54	55	56	57	58	59	60
61	62	63	64	65	66	67	68	69	70
71	72	73	74	75	76	77	78	79	80
81	82	83	84	85	86	87	88	89	90
91	92	93	94	95	96	97	98	99	100
101	102	103	104	105	106	107	108	109	110
111	112	113	114	115	116	117	118	119	120
121	122	123	124	125	126	127	128	129	130
131	132	133	134	135	136	137	138	139	140
141	142	143	144	145	146	147	148	149	150
151	152	153	154	155	156	157	158	159	160
161	162	163	164	165	166	167	168	169	170
171	172	173	174	175	176	177	178	179	180
181	182	183	184	185	186	187	188	189	190
191	192	193	194	195	196	197	198	199	200

112

? Where in each representation on pages 28 and 29 do you see 175? Where in each representation do you see 63? Where in each representation do you see 112?

SMH 30   thirty

▲ Math Words and Ideas, p. 30

Math Words and Ideas

Adding and Subtracting Tens and Hundreds

When you count by tens, you say the multiples of 10.

10, 20, 30, 40, 50, 60, 70, …

What happens when you add a multiple of 10 to a number or subtract a multiple of 10 from a number?

Look at what these third-grade students noticed in these problems.

$$\begin{array}{r} 46 \\ + 30 \\ \hline 76 \end{array}$$

Dwayne:
46 has 4 tens. I added 30. The sum is 76, which has 7 tens because I added 3 more tens.

$$\begin{array}{r} 138 \\ - 30 \\ \hline 108 \end{array}$$

Pilar:
I start with 3 tens in the 38 part of 138. So if I subtract 3 tens, then all I have left is the 1 hundred and the 8 ones, so the answer is 108.

$$\begin{array}{r} 356 \\ + 200 \\ \hline 556 \end{array}$$

Beatriz:
356 has 3 hundreds. I added 200. The sum is 556, which has 5 hundreds because I added 2 more hundreds.

? Solve these problems. Which digits change in the sums and differences?

$$\begin{array}{r} 565 \\ + 30 \end{array} \qquad \begin{array}{r} 565 \\ - 30 \end{array} \qquad \begin{array}{r} 565 \\ + 300 \end{array} \qquad \begin{array}{r} 565 \\ - 300 \end{array}$$

SMH 36   thirty-six

▲ Math Words and Ideas, p. 36

Math Words and Ideas

Coin Values and Equivalencies (page 1 of 2)

Math Words
- penny
- nickel
- dime

penny: 1¢ or $0.01	
front back	
nickel: 5¢ or $0.05	A nickel is worth the same as:
front back	
dime: 10¢ or $0.10	A dime is worth the same as:
front back	or
	 or

thirty-seven   **SMH 37**

▲ Math Words and Ideas, p. 37

Coin Values and Equivalencies (page 2 of 2)

Math Words
- quarter
- half dollar

quarter: 25¢ or $0.25	A quarter is worth the same as:
front / back	or

half-dollar: 50¢ or $0.50	A half-dollar is worth the same as:
front / back	or

? What are some other ways to make 25¢?
What are some other ways to make $0.50?

Math Words and Ideas, p. 38

Capture 5

You need
- 100 chart
- Change Cards (deck of 40)
- 12 chips of one color
- game piece for each player
- *Capture 5* Recording Sheet

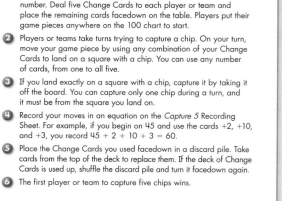

Play with a partner, or form a team with your partner and play another team of two players.

1. Place 12 chips on the 100 chart so that each chip is on a different number. Deal five Change Cards to each player or team and place the remaining cards facedown on the table. Players put their game pieces anywhere on the 100 chart to start.

2. Players or teams take turns trying to capture a chip. On your turn, move your game piece by using any combination of your Change Cards to land on a square with a chip. You can use any number of cards, from one to all five.

3. If you land exactly on a square with a chip, capture it by taking it off the board. You can capture only one chip during a turn, and it must be from the square you land on.

4. Record your moves in an equation on the *Capture 5* Recording Sheet. For example, if you begin on 45 and use the cards +2, +10, and +3, you record $45 + 2 + 10 + 3 = 60$.

5. Place the Change Cards you used facedown in a discard pile. Take cards from the top of the deck to replace them. If the deck of Change Cards is used up, shuffle the discard pile and turn it facedown again.

6. The first player or team to capture five chips wins.

Games, p. G3

Close to 100

You need
- Digit Cards (deck of 44)
- *Close to 100* Recording Sheet for each player

Play alone, with a partner, or in a small group.

1. Deal out six Digit Cards to each player.

2. Use any four cards to make two numbers; for example, 6 and 5 could make either 56 or 65. Wild cards can be used as any numeral. Try to make numbers that, when added, give you a total that is close to 100.

3. Write these two numbers and their total on the *Close to 100* Recording Sheet; for example, $42 + 56 = 98$.

4. Find your score. Your score is the difference between your total and 100. For example, if your total is 98, your score is 2. If your total is 105, your score is 5.

5. Put the cards you used in a discard pile. Keep the two cards you did not use for the next round.

6. For the next round, deal four new cards to each player. Make more numbers that come close to 100. When you run out of cards, shuffle the discard pile and use those cards again.

7. Five rounds make one game. Total your scores for the five rounds. The player with the LOWEST score wins.

Games, p. G5

Collect $2.00

You need
- pennies, dimes, and dollars

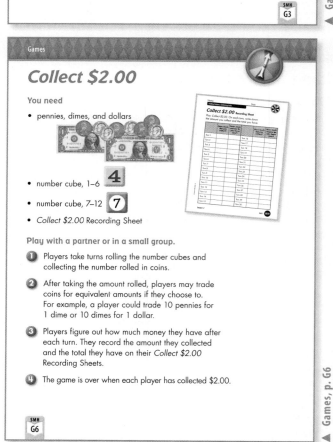

- number cube, 1–6 **4**
- number cube, 7–12 **7**
- *Collect $2.00* Recording Sheet

Play with a partner or in a small group.

1. Players take turns rolling the number cubes and collecting the number rolled in coins.

2. After taking the amount rolled, players may trade coins for equivalent amounts if they choose to. For example, a player could trade 10 pennies for 1 dime or 10 dimes for 1 dollar.

3. Players figure out how much money they have after each turn. They record the amount they collected and the total they have on their *Collect $2.00* Recording Sheets.

4. The game is over when each player has collected $2.00.

Games, p. G6

Games

Make a Dollar

You need

- Coin Cards (deck of 32)
- *Make a Dollar* Recording Sheet

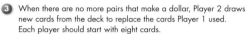
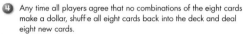

Play with one or two other players.

1. Deal eight Coin Cards faceup. Put the rest of the deck in a pile facedown.

2. Player 1 finds all pairs of cards that equal a dollar and records the equation for each pair on the *Make a Dollar* Recording Sheet.

3. When there are no more pairs that make a dollar, Player 2 draws new cards from the deck to replace the cards Player 1 used. Each player should start with eight cards.

4. Any time all players agree that no combinations of the eight cards make a dollar, shuffle all eight cards back into the deck and deal eight new cards.

5. The goal is to collect as many pairs of cards (dollars) as possible. The game ends when all the cards have been paired.

Scoring Variation

Make combinations of cards that equal any whole number of dollars. For example, a player could take three cards with 50¢, 70¢, and 80¢ for a total of two dollars. Your score at the end of the game is the number of dollars you have collected.

SMH
G16

▲ Games, p. G16

Index